Important Instruction

Students, Parents, and Teachers can use the URL or QR code provided below to access two full-length Lumos Geometry practice tests, hundreds of additional practice questions, educational videos, worksheets, mobile apps, standards information and more.

URL	QR Code
Visit the URL below and place the book access code **http://www.lumoslearning.com/a/tedbooks** **Access Code: HSGEO-83196-P**	

Developed by Expert Teachers

High School Geometry Review - Lumos Skills Mastery tedBook: Online Assessments and Practice Workbook

Contributing Author	-	John Eaton
Contributing Author	-	Tammie Rolf
Contributing Author	-	Lauren Inzelbuch
Contributing Author	-	Karen O Brien
Contributing Author	-	Donald Woods
Contributing Author	-	Janese Mott
Contributing Author	-	Paul Spinler
Contributing Author	-	Karen Russell
Contributing Author	-	Larry Russell
Executive Producer	-	Mukunda Krishnaswamy
Designer and Illustrator	-	Sowmya R.

ISBN-10: 1-949855-02-3

ISBN-13: 978-1-949855-02-9

Printed in the United States of America

For permissions and additional information contact us

Lumos Information Services, LLC
PO Box 1575, Piscataway, NJ 08855-1575
http://www.LumosLearning.com

Email: support@lumoslearning.com
Tel: (732) 384-0146
Fax: (866) 283-6471

Developed by Expert Teachers

Table of Contents

Online Program Benefits

Students*

- Two full-length Lumos Geometry practice tests
- Rigorous Standards Practice
- Technology-enhanced item types practice
- Additional learning resources such as videos and apps

Parents*

- You can review your student's online work by login to your parent account
- Pinpoint student areas of difficulty
- Develop custom lessons & assignments
- Access to High-Quality Question Bank

Teachers*

- Review the online work of your students
- Get insightful student reports
- Discover standards aligned videos, apps and books through EdSearch
- Easily access standards information along with the Coherence Map
- Create and share information about your classroom or school events

* Terms and Conditions apply

URL	QR Code
Visit the URL below and place the book access code **http://www.lumoslearning.com/a/tedbooks** **Access Code: HSGEO-83196-P**	

Start using the online resources included with this book today!

Introduction

This book is designed to provide practice of High School Geometry along with standards aligned to rigorous skills practice. Geometry is one of the credits that students must earn as a part of Mathematics credit requirement for High School Graduation requirements.

Unlike a traditional book, this Lumos tedBook offers two full-length practice tests both in the printed version as well as the Online version. Taking these tests will not only help students get a comprehensive review of standards assessed in Geometry but also become familiar with the technology-enhanced question types.

After students take the test online, educators can use the score report to assign specific lessons provided in this book.

Students will obtain a better understanding of each standard and improve on their weaknesses by practicing the content of this workbook. The lessons contain rigorous questions aligned to the state standards and substandards. Taking the time to work through the activities will afford students the ability to become proficient in each grade level standard.

How will Lumos StepUp® program help students in preparing for the end of course exams of High School Math credit programs?

The Lumos StepUp® program for High School Math courses includes

(a) Two Full-length practice tests

(b) Get realistic practice through Online Assessments. It gives students the opportunity to practice test-taking skills, familiarize with the format of the test and efficiently review the key topics. The results will give insights into your child's strengths and weaknesses in various content areas. These insights could be used to help your child strengthen their skills in topics where they are having difficulty. This test practice helps them improve speed and accuracy while taking the actual High School Math Assessments.

(c) StepUp® has great learning content with access to hundreds of activities and Online workbooks.

(d) Your child's work is carefully and meticulously tracked throughout the program. Easy-to-use, advanced and real-time reports will help you identify weak areas and tailor personalized learning plans for your child.

(e) The StepUp® program allows your child to prepare at a pace that is right for him or her. This student-centric approach, combined with instant feedback boosts student confidence and improves learning outcomes.

(f) StepUp® program can be accessed through a number of devices that include, PC, tablet and smart-phones and it is available 24×7. This convenience helps to enable anywhere learning.

Discover Engaging and Relevant Learning Resources

Lumos EdSearch is a safe search engine specifically designed for teachers and students. Using EdSearch, you can easily find thousands of standards-aligned learning resources such as questions, videos, lessons, worksheets and apps. Teachers can use EdSearch to create custom resource kits to perfectly match their lesson objective and assign them to one or more students in their classroom.

To access the EdSearch tool, use the search box after you log into Lumos StepUp or use the link provided below.

http://www.lumoslearning.com/a/edsearchb	

The Lumos Standards Coherence map provides information about previous level, next level and related standards. It helps educators and students visually explore learning standards. It's an effective tool to help students progress through the learning objectives. Teachers can use this tool to develop their own pacing charts and lesson plans. Educators can also use the coherence map to get deep insights into why a student is struggling in a specific learning objective.

Teachers can access the Coherence maps after logging into the StepUp Teacher Portal or use the link provided below.

http://www.lumoslearning.com/a/coherence-map	

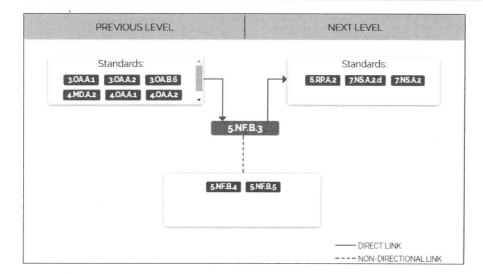

How to use this book effectively

The Lumos Program is a flexible learning tool. It can be adapted to suit a student's skill level and the time available to practice before standardized tests. Here are some tips to help you use this book and the online resources effectively:

Students

- The standards in each book can be practiced in the order designed, or in the order you prefer.
- Complete all problems in each workbook.
- Take the first practice assessment online which has 2 parts in Math.
- Have open-ended questions evaluated by a teacher or parent, keeping in mind the scoring rubrics.
- Take the second practice assessment as you get close to the official test date. This will also have 2 parts in Math.
- Complete the test in a quiet place, following the test guidelines. Practice tests provide you an opportunity to improve your test taking skills and to review topics included in the test.

Parents

- Help your child use Lumos StepUp® Online Assessments by following the instructions in "Access Online Program" section.
- You can review your student's online work by login to your parent account.
- You can also conveniently access student progress report on your mobile devices by downloading the Lumos StepUp app. Please follow directions provided in "How can I Download the App?" section in Lumos StepUp® Mobile App FAQ For Parents and Teachers.

1) **The day before the test,** make sure you get a good night's sleep.

2) **On the day of the test,** be sure to eat a good hearty breakfast! Also, be sure to arrive at school on time.

3) **During the test:**

- **Read every question carefully.**

  - Do not spend too much time on any one question. Work steadily through all questions in the section.
  - Attempt all of the questions even if you are not sure of some answers.
  - If you run into a difficult question, eliminate as many choices as you can and then pick the best one from the remaining choices. Intelligent guessing will help you increase your score.
  - Also, mark the question so that if you have extra time, you can return to it after you reach the end of the section.
  - Some questions may refer to a graph, chart, or other kind of picture. Carefully review the infographics before answering the question.
  - Be sure to include explanations for your written responses and show all work.

- **While Answering TECR questions.**

  - Read the directions of each question. Some might ask you to drag something, others to select, and still others to highlight. Follow all instructions of the question (or questions if it is in multiple parts)

Here are some reminders for when you are taking the Practice Test.

To answer the questions on the test, use the directions given in the question. If you do not know the answer to a question, skip it and go on to the next question. If time permits, you may return to questions in this session only. Do your best to answer every question.

Practice Test 1

1. What is the measure of ∠GEH where E lies on $\overleftrightarrow{DF}$, ∠DEG = 50°, and $\overline{EH}$ bisects ∠FEG ?

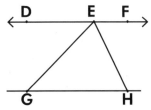

2. A student has given the following definition of perpendicular lines, find and fix the error with an explanation:

   Two lines that never intersect are known as perpendicular lines. Since lines continue in both directions for an infinite length, they will never intersect.

3. Fill in the table by matching the shape with the correct transformation of the shape below:

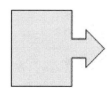

	Dilation	Rotation 90° counterclockwise	Rotation 90° clockwise
	○	○	○
	○	○	○
	○	○	○

4. What combination of transformations will map the image ABCD onto A'B'C'D'?

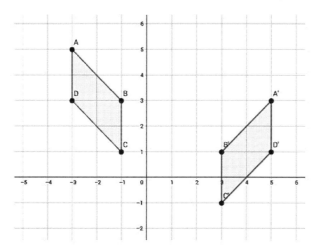

   Ⓐ Reflection over the x-axis and translate 2 down
   Ⓑ Translate to the right 4 and down 2
   Ⓒ Reflection over the x = 1 and a translation two units down
   Ⓓ Reflection over the line y = 1 and translate 4 to the left

5. What transformation moves any point A counterclockwise to a point B where PA=PB and ∠APB=0?

6. Which of the following show a translation of three units to the left and two units down of the shape ABCD ?

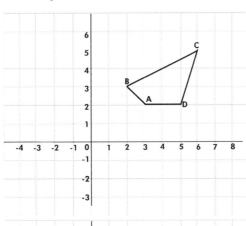

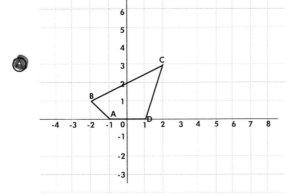

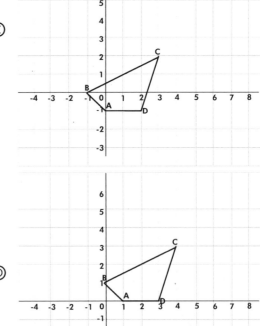

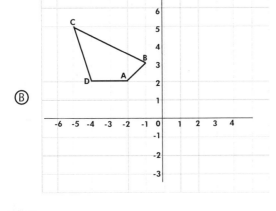

7. Write the best word to fill in the blank in this sentence:
   In geometry, a solid object is a set of points that forms a figure that has _____ dimension(s).

   Ⓐ one
   Ⓑ two
   Ⓒ three
   Ⓓ four

8. Suppose SUWV $\longrightarrow$ VKLM in the figure below. What is the translation rule?

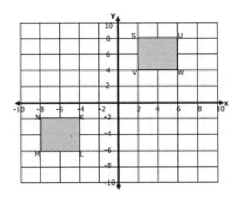

   Ⓐ (x, y)$\longrightarrow$(x - 10, y - 10)
   Ⓑ (x, y)$\longrightarrow$ (x + 10, y - 10)
   Ⓒ (x, y)$\longrightarrow$(x - 10, y + 10)
   Ⓓ (x, y)$\longrightarrow$(x + 10, y + 10)

9. Which triangle in the figure below is the result of translating △ABC using the rule (x, y)$\longrightarrow$(x+5, y-2)?

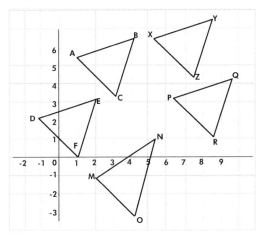

   Ⓐ △DEF
   Ⓑ △MNO
   Ⓒ △PQR
   Ⓓ △XYZ

10. Point W(6, -6) in the figure below is reflecting over the line y=x creating point W' and then reflected across the x-axis creating point W". What translation rule (not a reflection) will result in point being transformed back to point W?

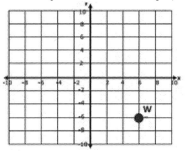

Ⓐ (x, y) ⟶ (x-12, y)
Ⓑ (x, y) ⟶ (x, y-12)
Ⓒ (x, y) ⟶ (-x, y)
Ⓓ (x, y) ⟶ (x, -y)

11. Triangle B was transformed with two separate transformations to create triangle B". What are the two transformations?

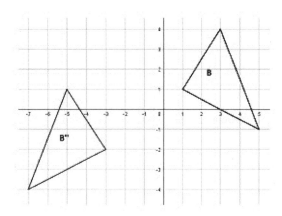

Ⓐ down 3 , reflection across x = -1
Ⓑ down 2, reflection across x = 1
Ⓒ down 4, reflection across x = 1
Ⓓ up 3, reflection across x = -1

12. An airplane is flying 800 miles per hour. To the nearest foot, how many feet per second is this?

Ⓐ 70,400
Ⓑ 1,173
Ⓒ 20
Ⓓ 1,111

13. Every month, a group of 36 students write essays in a writing class. Each student writes 4 essays, and each essay contains an average of 800 words. How many words do the students write each month?

Ⓐ 144,000
Ⓑ 28,800
Ⓒ 3,200
🅓 115,200

14. Given ΔABC on the coordinate plane below.

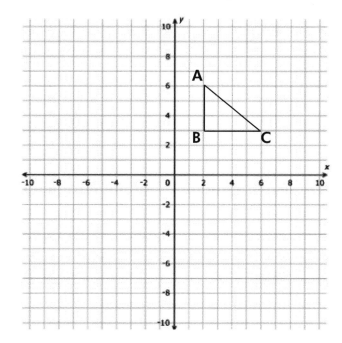

a. Draw ΔA'B'C' by transforming ΔABC as follows:
a dilation centered at the origin with a scale factor of two, followed by a reflection across the x-axis, and finally a rotation of 180 degrees clockwise about the origin.

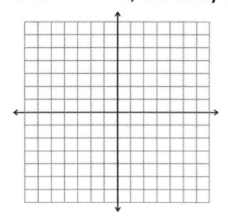

b. State if the two triangles are congruent, similar, or neither and support your conclusion based on sound geometric principals.

15. If the sides can be moved in any way you wish, is it possible to reconstruct the sides of the polygon below so the given circle is inscribed? Support your argument by attempting to reconstruct the polygon showing that you can or cannot do it, then explain why you could or could not perform the reconstruction required.

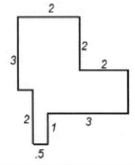
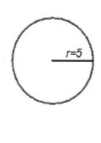

16. Let $0 < \dfrac{a^2 - b^2}{a + b} < 1$ where a and b are nonzero real numbers. Which of the following statements apply for a and b ?

ⓐ a has to be greater than b but less than b + 1.
ⓑ a has to be less than b but greater than b + 1.
ⓒ a has to be greater than b but less than b + 1.
ⓓ There are no values that will satisfy the combined inequality.

17. Given right triangle ΔABC below with corresponding sides a,b,c. Which of the following statements are true?

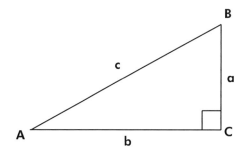

ⓐ $\dfrac{\cos A}{\sin A} = \dfrac{a}{b}$

ⓑ $\dfrac{\tan B}{\sin B} = \dfrac{c}{a}$

ⓒ $\sin C = \cos B$

ⓓ $\cos A = \tan B$

18. The diagram below shows a circle with center O and a right triangle ΔXYZ, where Y is a right angle and side YZ passes through the center of circle O. Which of the following best represents the circumference of circle O ?

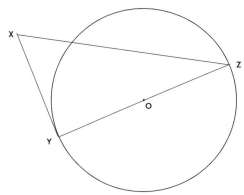

ⓐ $\pi(XY) \cdot \tan X$
ⓑ $\pi(YZ) \cdot \cos X$
ⓒ $\pi[(XY) \cdot \tan X]^2$
ⓓ $\pi[(YZ) \cdot \cos X]^2$

19. Which of the following statements are true for sine and cosine? Mark all that apply.

(A) $\cos\frac{\pi}{3} = \sin\frac{\pi}{6}$

(B) $\cos\frac{\pi}{12} = \sin\frac{11}{12}\pi$

(C) $\sin\frac{\pi}{4} = \cos\frac{\pi}{4}$

(D) $\sin\frac{\pi}{5} = \cos\frac{\pi}{5}\pi$

20. Which of the following statements is true for the right triangle given below? Mark all that apply.

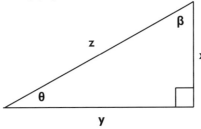

(A) $\cos\theta = \sin(45^0 + \beta)$
(B) $\sin\theta = \cos(90^0 - \beta)$
(C) $\sin\theta = \cos(45^0 + \beta)$
(D) $\cos\theta = \sin(90^0 - \beta)$

21. Alex wants to swim across a river but will only do so if the width of the river is 160 meters or less. From the river's bank he looks straight across and spots a tree on the other side of the river's bank. Then, Alex walks 200 meters down river and again sees the same tree on the other side of the river. At that time, his line of site from his starting position to the tree on the other side of the river measures 38⁰. Will Alex swim across the river?

(A) No, since he will have to swim 200 meters.
(B) No, since he will have to swim 256 meters.
(C) Yes, since he will only have to swim 156 meters.
(D) Yes, since he will only have to swim 117 meters.

22. You are standing at a certain horizontal distance from the base of a building that is perpendicular to level ground. You observe an angle of elevation from your feet to the top of the building of 30⁰. Then you walk 100 feet straight towards the building and stop short of reaching the building to tie your shoes. At that point you observe and angle of elevation to the top of the building of 60⁰. To the nearest foot, how tall is the building?

(A) 87 feet
(B) 100 feet
(C) 400 feet
(D) 500 feet

23. A rectangular box with no top is to be made from a rectangular piece of cardboard that has a length of 11 inches and a width of 8 inches, by cutting square corners with equal sides and turning the sides up to form the box. In order to maximize the volume of the box you need to cut the squares at a certain length. Which of the following will be a dimension of the rectangular box? Mark all that apply.

Ⓐ 11-2x
Ⓑ 11-x
Ⓒ 8-2x
Ⓓ 8-x

24. A right circular cone is inscribed in a sphere that has a radius of r. The radius of the cone and the radius of the sphere are the same. Which of the following expressions will determine the slant height l of the right circular cone?

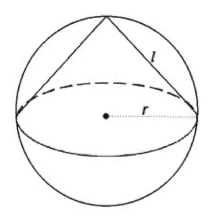

Ⓐ $l^2 = r^2 + r^2$

Ⓑ $l = \left(\frac{\pi}{2}\right)r$

Ⓒ $l = r$

Ⓓ $l = 2r \sin\left(\frac{\pi}{4}\right)$

25. What is the translation rule and the scale factor of the dilation as Circle F → Circle F'?

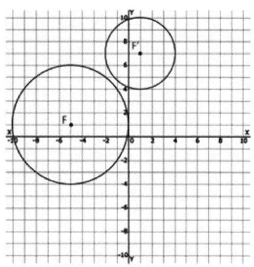

Enter your answer in the form (x,y) → $\frac{a}{b}$ (x+h,y+k) where a, b, h, and k are integers, and in your own words, indicate how you arrived at the answer giving proper steps or justification.

26. The figure below shows circle O, the measure of central angle ∠XOZ, and inscribed angle ∠XYZ. What is m ∠XYZ?

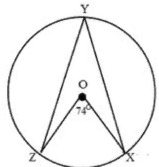

27. Two passengers are located at fixed distances R and 2R from the axis about which an amusement park ride rotates, such that they travel in circular paths. Answer the following questions to determine the ratio of the arc lengths traveled by the riders during the same time interval.

(a) During a certain time interval, it is observed that the ride rotates through an angle $\theta = \frac{\pi}{4}$. Find the distance traveled along the arc by the rider located R from the ride axis.

(b) Determine the distance traveled along the arc by the rider located 2R from the ride axis during this same time interval.

(c) Find the ratio of the distance traveled by the rider in (b) to the traveled by the rider in (a).

28. What is the equation of a circle, in the form, $(x-h)^2+(y-k)^2=r^2$, if the center of the circle is at the point $(-5,-3)$ and the point $(1,3)$ is on the circle? Enter your answer, in the correct form, and in your own words, indicate how you arrived at the answer giving proper steps or justification.

29. What is the equation of the parabola if the focus is at point (8, 5) and the equation of the directrix is y=3? Enter your answer in vertex form, y=a(x−h)²+k, and in your own words, indicate how you arrived at the answer giving proper steps or justification.

30. A line segment has endpoints at M (1, 7) and N (-3, -1). What is the length of the segment?

Ⓐ $2\sqrt{3}$ units

Ⓑ 12 units

Ⓒ $4\sqrt{5}$ units

Ⓓ $16\sqrt{5}$ units

31. A ball with radius 6 cm just fits inside a cylindrical can with radius of 6 cm and height 10 cm. How much empty space is left in the can?

Ⓐ 18π cm³

Ⓑ 36π cm³

Ⓒ 54π cm³

Ⓓ 72π cm³

32. A hemisphere with radius 3 cm sits atop a cone of equal diameter and height of 10 cm as shown in the diagram below. Find the combined volume of the composite object.

Ⓐ 24π cm³

Ⓑ 36π cm³

Ⓒ 48π cm³

Ⓓ 60π cm³

33. **Answer the following question:**
    Given the sets of letters U = {a,b,c,d,e,f,g,h,i,j,k,l,m,n,o,p,q,r,s,t,u,v,w,x,y,z},
    A = {a,e,i,o,u,y}, B = {a,d,g,j,m,p,s,v,y}, and C = {a.e.i, m,q,u,y}.

    How many elements are in the set :A ∩ :C ? Enter your answer, and in your own words, indicate how you arrived at the answer giving proper steps or justification.

34. Suppose the probability that event A occurs is $\frac{7}{15}$, the probability that event B occurs is $\frac{3}{5}$, and the probability that both events A and B occur is $\frac{2}{9}$. What is the probability that event A or event B occurs?

    Ⓐ $\frac{48}{45}$

    Ⓑ $\frac{26}{45}$

    Ⓒ $\frac{38}{45}$

    Ⓓ $\frac{4}{45}$

35. Your teacher brought candy for the class on Halloween but somehow miscalculated and has enough for all the students except for one. You collectively decided that you would all pick a number and whoever picks the number furthest away from the one randomly generated by the teacher's graphing calculator will not get a piece of candy. In what way should the teacher choose a number from a random number generator?

36. There is a game of chance where the outcome is a random integer from 1 to 8. You can place one of two bets in the game. Bet A costs $10 to place. If the random integer outcome is a 5, the bet returns a payout of $98. Otherwise it returns nothing. Bet B costs $8 to place. If the random integer outcome is an even number, the bet returns a payout of $24. Otherwise, it returns nothing. Which bet is a better deal?

Ⓐ Bet A
Ⓑ Bet B
Ⓒ The bets have the same net value
Ⓓ Cannot be determined

Here are some reminders for when you are taking the Practice Test.

To answer the questions on the test, use the directions given in the question. If you do not know the answer to a question, skip it and go on to the next question. If time permits, you may return to questions in this session only. Do your best to answer every question.

Practice Test 2

1. In the figure below points E, F, and H are collinear and points E, G, and J are collinear. Can ∠FGJ be found using the information that is given? If so find the measure of the angle using a geometric argument. If not state why.

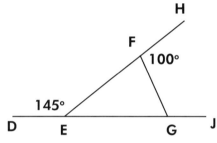

2. Match the regular polygon with the correct rotational degree measure that will map the polygon onto itself.

	120°	90°	72°	60°
Equilateral triangle				
Square				
Regular pentagon				
Regular hexagon				

3. Which of the following triangles is congruent to the triangle below due to a rotation of 180 degrees?

Ⓐ

Ⓑ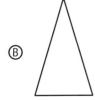

Ⓒ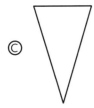

Ⓓ

4. Which of the following states "If two angles and the included side of one triangle are equal to the corresponding angles and side of another triangle, the triangles are congruent."

Ⓐ SAS postulate
Ⓑ ASA postulate
Ⓒ SSS postulate
Ⓓ AAS postulate

5.

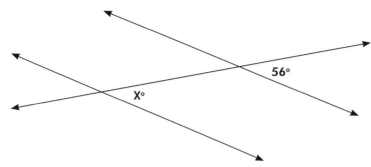

Joe believes that the measure of angle X is 34 degrees because the angles are complementary. Jack says that the measure of angle X is 56 degrees because the angles are corresponding angles. Who is correct?

6. Triangle ABC is an isosceles triangle with angle measures of 65 degrees and 50 degrees. Henry says that the third angle has a measure of 65 degrees. Mark says that the third angle must have a measure of 50 degrees. Who is correct?

7. The elliptical figure shown below is translated up 5 units and to the right 5 units. How do the pre-image and the post-image compare?

Ⓐ They are congruent
Ⓑ The pre-image is smaller
Ⓒ The post-image is smaller
Ⓓ Impossible to tell

8. △ ABC was transformed into A'B'C' . Verify that the transformation is a rigid motion by stating why the two triangles are congruent, or state that the transformation is not a rigid motion.

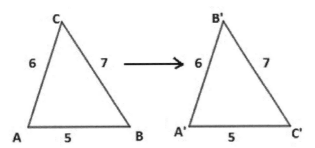

  Ⓐ SSS
  Ⓑ ASA
  Ⓒ SAS
  Ⓓ Not a rigid motion

9. Which triangle congruence method can we use to say that △ABC → △DEC represents some type of rigid motion?

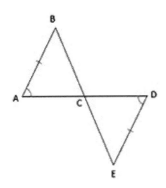

  Ⓐ ASA
  Ⓑ SSS
  Ⓒ SAS
  Ⓓ AAS

10. Given: m∠2 = m∠6 , m∠1 = m∠5.
    These angles are pairs of corresponding angles which are congruent. What can we say about line u and line v?

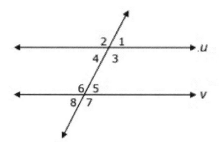

Ⓐ u ≅ v
Ⓑ u ⊥ v
Ⓒ u || v
Ⓓ Cannot make any conclusions

11. Given: m∠4 = m∠6; m∠1 = m∠3; ∠DEB ≅ ∠DCB. What can we say about ΔBED and ΔBAD ?

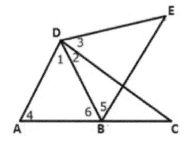

Ⓐ ΔBED ~ ΔBAD
Ⓑ ΔBED ~ ΔABD
Ⓒ ΔBDE ≅ ΔBAD
Ⓓ ΔBED ~ ΔBDA

12. Which function squares the input variable, then triples that value, adds five times the input variable and then subtracts twelve?

Ⓐ $f(x)=-3x^2+5x-12$
Ⓑ $f(x)=3x^2+5x-12$
Ⓒ $f(x)=3x^2-5x-12$
Ⓓ $f(x)=3x^2+5x+12$

13. **During an Air Show, an acrobatic plane dives toward the ground and then veers upward just above ground level. The path of the parabolic flight is shown below. What does the vertex of the parabolic path represent?**

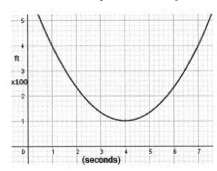

Ⓐ The plane is at its maximum height of 100 feet above the ground at 4 seconds.
Ⓑ The plane is at its minimum height of 100 feet above the ground at 4 seconds.
Ⓒ The plane is at its maximum height of 400 feet above the ground at 1 seconds.
Ⓓ The plane is at its minimum height of 400 feet above the ground at 1 seconds

14. **The graph of $f(x) = \frac{1}{4}x^3 - x^2 - x + 1$ is shown below. Over which interval is f(x) decreasing?**

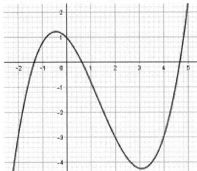

(3.10, ∞)
(-4.26, 1.23)
(-0.43, 3.10)
(-∞, 3. -0.43)

15. A company wants to maximize the profit it makes for selling two types of sodas. A carton of grape soda returns a profit of $1.75 and a carton of cherry soda returns a profit of $2.25. Your firm has been hired to help the company maximize its profit and found the following constraints that must be applied.

1. Cartons of both sodas should not exceed 1500 cartons a week.
2. The demand for cherry sodas cannot exceed half of the demand for grape sodas.
3. The company should produce grape sodas at a level that is less than or equal to 500 cartons plus twice the production level for cherry sodas.

The graph of the shaded region is subjected to the given constraints where x is the number of cartons of grape soda, and y is the number of cartons of cherry soda.

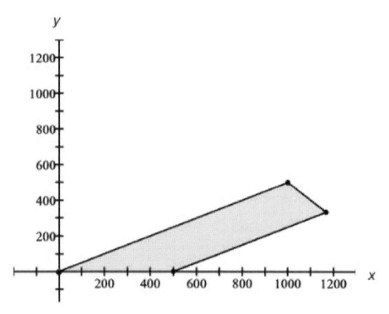

Which of the following inequalities does not apply to the graph of the constraints?

Ⓐ x+y ≤ 1500
Ⓑ x ≤ 500+2y
Ⓒ 1.75x + 2.25y ≤ 1500
Ⓓ y ≤ $\frac{1}{2}$x

16. **You are trying to disprove that 2≠ 1 after your friend shows you the following nine step proof that 2 = 1.**

1. $a=b$	assumption
2. $a^2=b^2$	square both sides
3. $a^2-b^2=b^2-b^2$	subtract both sides by b^2
4. $(a-b)(a+b)=b(b-b)$	factor both sides
5. $(a-b)(a+b)=b(a-b)$	substitute b with a
6. $(a+b)=b$	cancel $(a-b)$ on both sides
7. $(b+b)=b$	substitute a with b
8. $2b=b$	add $b+b$
9. $2=1$	cancel b on both sides

Is it possible for you to disprove your friends conjecture? Provide justification to support your conclusion.

17. If triangle DEF is a dilation of triangle ABC, what is the scale factor?

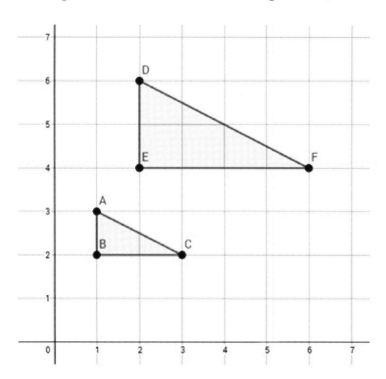

Ⓐ 0.5
Ⓑ 1
Ⓒ 2
Ⓓ -2

18. The ratio of length in an image to the preimage is known as what?

Ⓐ Dilation
Ⓑ Scale factor
Ⓒ Reflection
Ⓓ Orientation

19. A line segment has the endpoints (3, 2) and (1, 2). Which pair of endpoints could be for an image that was dilated by a scale factor of 2 with an unknown center?

Ⓐ (0, 1) and (2, 3)
Ⓑ (2, 2) and (0, 2)
Ⓒ (0, 2) and (4, 2)
Ⓓ (1, 2) and (3, 2)

20. Which of the following images shows a dilation with a scale factor of 0.5?

Ⓐ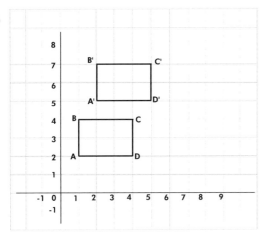

Ⓑ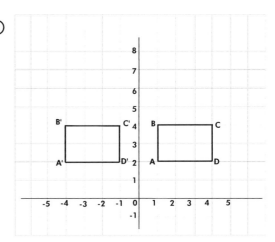

Ⓒ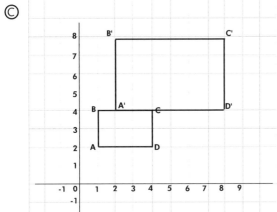

Ⓓ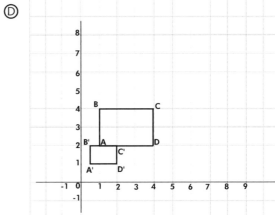

21. Which of the following triangles would not be similar to triangle ABC?

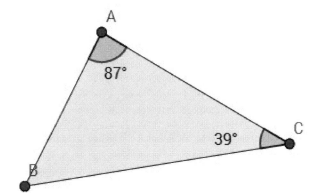

Ⓐ

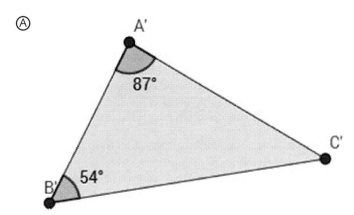

Ⓑ

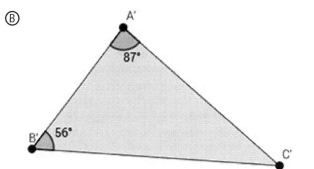

Ⓒ

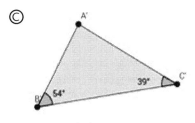

Ⓓ

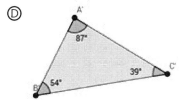

22. Complete the steps below to illustrate the effect of the scale factor on the image produced by a dilation

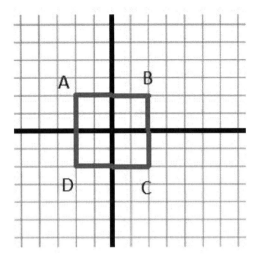

a) On the graph, sketch the dilation of ABCD centered at the origin with a scale factor of 2.

b) On the graph, sketch the dilation of ABCD centered at the origin with a scale factor of ½.

c) What conclusion can you draw from this exercise?
Explain in detail.

23. ΔABC and ΔQDE are right triangles. If ∠C=25° and ∠D=65°, ∠B=90° and ∠Q=90°, which similarity statement is true?

    Ⓐ ΔABC ~ ΔDEQ
    Ⓑ ΔABC ~ ΔDQE
    Ⓒ ΔABC ~ ΔQDE
    Ⓓ ΔBAC ~ ΔDQE

24. ΔLMN has a segment, $\overline{XY}$ that is drawn inside the triangle and parallel to side LN and with point X on $\overline{LM}$. If m∠MXY=40° and m∠MLN=40°, what is the similarity statement for the two triangles.?

    Ⓐ ΔLMN ~ ΔMYX
    Ⓑ ΔLMN ~ ΔMXY
    Ⓒ ΔLMN ~ ΔYMX
    Ⓓ ΔLMN ~ ΔXMY

25. Using a dilation of 3/2 and given the diagram below showing circles A and B centered at the points indicated, Which of the following correctly describes the translation from circle A to circle B?

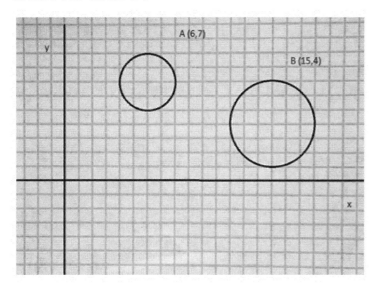

    Ⓐ x' = x - 3 , y' = y + 9
    Ⓑ x' = x + 3 , y' = y - 9
    Ⓒ x' = x + 9 , y' = y - 3
    Ⓓ x' = x - 9 , y' = y + 3

26. Two passengers are located at fixed distances R and 2R from the axis about which an amusement park ride rotates, such that they travel in circular paths. Answer the following questions to determine the ratio of the arc lengths traveled by the riders during the same time interval.

a) During a certain time interval, it is observed that the ride rotates through an angle $\theta = \frac{\pi}{4}$. Find the distance traveled along the arc by the rider located R from the ride axis.

b) Determine the distance traveled along the arc by the rider located 2R from the ride axis during this same time interval.

c) Find the ratio of the distance traveled by the rider in b) to that traveled by the rider in a).

27. Complete the table below relating arc radius (r), arc angle θ, arc length, and the area of the sector. Leave your answer in terms of π.

r	θ	Length	Area
12 cm	$\frac{\pi}{4}$		
5 cm		$\frac{10\pi}{3}$ cm	

28. A circle has its center at the point (−5,−8) and passes through the point (2,−32). Does the circle contain the point (2,16)? Enter your answer, and in your own words, indicate how you arrived at the answer giving proper steps or justification.

29. What is the equation, in standard form, of the line that passes through the point (4,7), and is parallel to the line with the equation y=-5x+3? Enter your answer, in standard form, and in your own words, indicate how you arrived at the answer giving proper steps or justification.

30. A directed line segment is a line segment from one point to another point in the coordinate plane. When using directed line segments, pay close attention to the beginning and endpoints of the line.

   The endpoints of $\overline{AB}$ are (1, -3) and (4,2). Find the midpoint of the segment.

Ⓐ $(\frac{3}{2}, \frac{5}{2})$

Ⓑ $(\frac{5}{2}, \frac{-1}{2})$

Ⓒ $(\frac{3}{2}, \frac{-1}{2})$

Ⓓ (5, -1)

31. Find the volume of a cylinder that is the result of rotating the rectangle below around either of its heights. Leave the answer in terms of π.

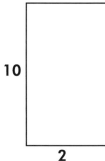

10

2

32. Match the shape of the cross sections with the given 3D object in the list shown below.

	Triangle	Circle	Rectangle
Cone			
Cylinder			
Sphere			

33. Suppose you are tossing three coins in a game of chance. To win the game, you must throw three heads. In the first toss, you get a head. In the second toss, you get another head. What is the probability of throwing a third head? Enter your answer, and in your own words, indicate how you arrived at the answer giving proper steps or justification.

34. A report shows that in a high school with 400 students, there are 40% girls. The report says that 20% of the students in the school wear glasses. It is also known that 10% of the boys wear glasses. How many boys wear glasses?

Ⓐ 24
Ⓑ 240
Ⓒ 16
Ⓓ 160

35. McDonald's has come up with a new menu item that they think will appeal to 30% of their customers. The executives have decided that the chances that the item will be bought by a random person or not be bought by a random person are 50%. Are they correct or incorrect in their assumption?

36. Mike and John are the captains of two baseball teams. They roll a die to decide which team will bat first. If the die lands on an odd number, Mike's team will bat first. Otherwise, John's team will bat first. Which statement is correct about the fairness of this method?

Ⓐ The method is not fair because Mike's team will always bat first.
Ⓑ The method is fair because John's team has a better chance to bat first.
Ⓒ The method is fair because each team has an equal chance to bat first.
Ⓓ The method is not fair because there are more odd numbers on the die.

Practice Test 1
Answer Key & Detailed Explanations

<table>
<tr><th>Question No.</th><th>Answer</th><th>Detailed Explanation</th></tr>
<tr><td>1</td><td></td><td>∠FEG and ∠DEG are supplementary since they form a linear pair, so ∠FEG=180°−50°=130° Also, since $\overline{EH}$ bisects ∠FEG we take one-half ∠FEG, ∠GEH= $\frac{130°}{2}$ =65°.</td></tr>
<tr><td>2</td><td></td><td>The student has given the definition for parallel lines. Since the question was referring to perpendicular lines the definition needs to change to "Two lines that intersect at 90 degrees, or right angles, are known as perpendicular".</td></tr>
<tr><td>3</td><td></td><td>Rotations are turns, clockwise goes to the right one 90 degree rotation, and clockwise goes to the left one 90 degree rotation. A dilation is when an image gets bigger or smaller, in this case, smaller.
<table>
<tr><th></th><th>Dilation</th><th>Rotation 90° counterclockwise</th><th>Rotation 90° clockwise</th></tr>
<tr><td>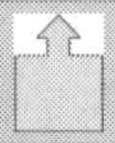</td><td>○</td><td>●</td><td>○</td></tr>
<tr><td>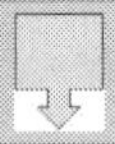</td><td>○</td><td>○</td><td>●</td></tr>
<tr><td>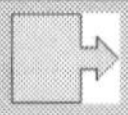</td><td>●</td><td>○</td><td>○</td></tr>
</table></td></tr>
<tr><td>4</td><td>C</td><td>The reflection over x = 1 is able to match the shapes, however it needs to be translated, or slide two units down in order to map onto itself.</td></tr>
<tr><td>5</td><td></td><td>Rotation. Only a rotation uses angles (θ) in order to transform a shape or point.</td></tr>
<tr><td>6</td><td>A</td><td>A translation will move, or slide the shape. In this case all points go three to the left and two down.</td></tr>
<tr><td>7</td><td>C</td><td>In geometry, a solid object is a set of points that forms a figure that has three dimensions. The three dimensions are called width, depth and height. Some examples of solids include cubes, pyramids, spheres, cylinders, and prisms.</td></tr>
<tr><td>8</td><td>A</td><td>We are asked to find the translation rule for SUWV → VKLM in the given figure. Since the figure is translated, we can find the translation rule by looking at the translation of a pair of corresponding points between the pre-image and the image. The points S and N correspond. Using the coordinates of each point, the translation rule for S → N follows the translation rule for (2, 8) → (-8,-2). Notice that the value of each component of the coordinates decreases by 10. Therefore, the translation rule for the figure is (x, y) → (x-10, y-10).</td></tr>
</table>

Question No.	Answer	Detailed Explanation
9	C	The question asks us which triangle in the figure below is the result of translating ΔABC using the rule (x, y)→(x+5, y-2). First of all, is not the same shape as ΔABC. Translations are rigid motions, which means the size and shape does not change. ΔDEF is the result of the rule (x, y)→(x-2, y-2). ΔXYZ is the result of the rule (x, y)→(x+4, y+1). ΔPQR is the result of the rule (x, y)→(x+5, y-2) as shown in the figure below. 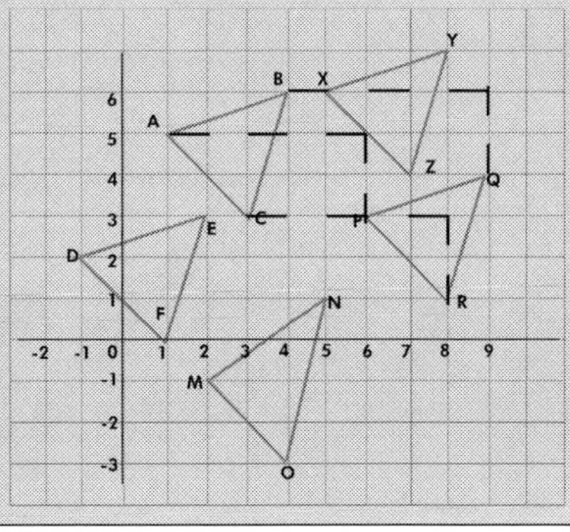
10	B	The question states that point p W(6, -6) p is reflected across the origin creating point W ' and then reflected across the x-axis creating point W". We are asked what translation rule (not a reflection) will result in point W" being transformed back to point W. The figure below shows the result of the two reflections. Notice that a reflection across the x-axis would place point W" back onto the original position, but the question specifically asks us to provide a translation rule that is not a reflection. Note that if point W" is translated downward 12 units, it will be in the original position. Therefore, the rule is (x, y)→(x, y-12). 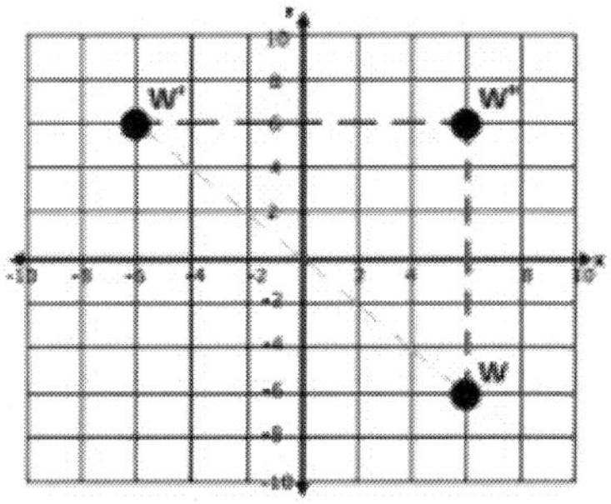

Question No.	Answer	Detailed Explanation
11	A	The figure below shows that to create triangle B'' from triangle B using two transformation. The first one is a translation down 3 units and the second one is a reflection x = -1. 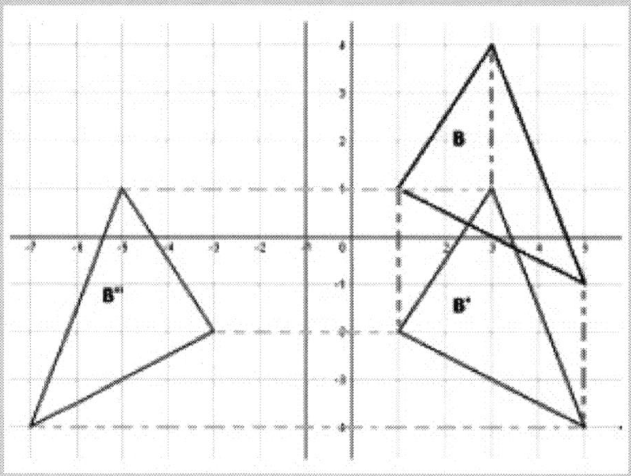
12	B	There is 5,280 feet per mile, 60 minutes per hour, and 60 seconds per minute. Convert miles per hour to feet per second. $$\frac{800\ miles}{hour} * \frac{5280\ feet}{mile} * \frac{1\ hour}{60\ minutes} * \frac{1\ minutes}{60\ seconds}$$ Cancel the units. Then, multiply and divide. $$\frac{800\ \cancel{miles}}{\cancel{hour}} * \frac{5280\ feet}{\cancel{mile}} * \frac{1\ \cancel{hour}}{60\ \cancel{minutes}} * \frac{1\ \cancel{minutes}}{60\ seconds} = 1173.\overline{3}$$
13	D	Multiply 36*4*800 = 115,200 The units convert as follows: $$\frac{36\ \cancel{students}}{1} * \frac{4\ \cancel{essays}}{\cancel{student}} * \frac{800\ words}{\cancel{essay}} = 115,200\ words$$
14		a. The graph of ΔA'B'C'. 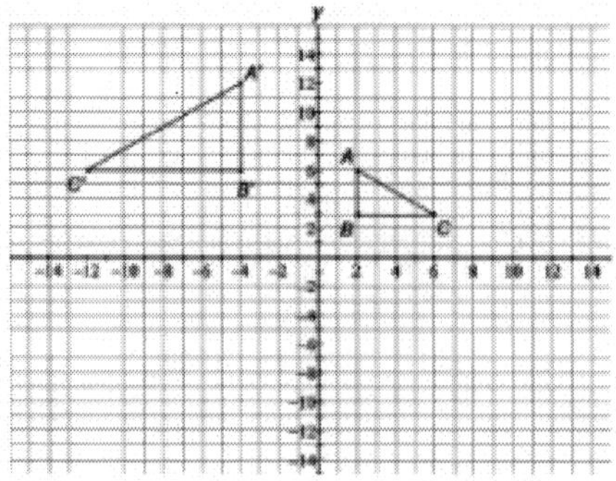 b. ΔABC Is similar to ΔA'B'C'. Clearly the triangles are not congruent by virtue of the dilation of ΔABC. However, the reflection and rotation of ΔABC does not change the corresponding angles to change or the corresponding sides to be out of proportion due to the dilation.

Question No.	Answer	Detailed Explanation
15		In order for the circle to be inscribed in the square, the sides of the square will have to be 5 units each for a perimeter of 20 units. Since the perimeter of the polygon is 26 units. It is not possible to reconstruct the polygon into a square since the sum of the sides is 26.
16	A	The correct answer is A. The inequality $\frac{a^2 - b^2}{a + b}$ should always be defined since a and b are nonzero real numbers, so $a+b \neq 0$. Simplifying our middle expression we get $$0 < \frac{a^2 - b^2}{a + b} < 1 \ , \ 0 < \frac{(a - b)(a + b)}{a + b} < 1, \ 0 < a-b < 1.$$ Solving the inequality for a we get $0 < a-b < 1$ this means $a-b > 0$ and $a-b < 1$ $a > b$ and $a < b+1$.
17	B	Using $\tan B = \frac{b}{a}$ and $\sin B = \frac{b}{c}$, we get, $\frac{\tan B}{\sin B} = \frac{\frac{b}{a}}{\frac{b}{c}} = \frac{b}{a} * \frac{c}{b} = \frac{c}{a}$.
18	A	The correct answer is A. The real goal is to find the length of side YZ since half of its' length will be the radius of the circle. Then, we us $C=2\pi r$ to get the circumference of the circle. Using the trigonometric ratio for tangent we get, $$\tan \theta = \frac{\text{opposite side}}{\text{adjacent side}}, \ \tan X = \frac{YZ}{XY}$$ Next solving for YZ we get, $\tan X = \frac{YZ}{XY}$, $YZ = (XY) \tan X$. Now the radius for the circle is $r = \frac{1}{2}(XY) \tan X$, so the circumference of the circle becomes, $C = 2\pi r$ $C = 2\pi * \frac{1}{2}(XY) \tan X = \pi(XY) \tan X$
19	A & C	The correct answers are A and C. Sine and Cosine are called functions which means, $$\sin\theta = \cos\left(\frac{\pi}{2} = \theta\right) \text{and} \cos\theta = \sin\left(\frac{\pi}{2} = \theta\right).$$ Now $\cos\frac{\pi}{3} = \sin\left(\frac{\pi}{2} - \frac{\pi}{3}\right) = \sin\left(\frac{3\pi}{6} - \frac{2\pi}{6}\right) = \sin\frac{\pi}{6}$. Similarly, $\cos\frac{\pi}{4} = \sin\left(\frac{\pi}{2} - \frac{\pi}{4}\right) = \sin\left(\frac{2\pi}{4} - \frac{\pi}{4}\right) = \sin\frac{\pi}{4}$.

Question No.	Answer	Detailed Explanation
20	B & D	The correct answers are B and D. Angles θ and β complementary so, $\theta+\beta=90^0$, then $\theta=90^0-\beta$ Now, using the sum/difference formula for cosine we get answer B. $\cos(90^0-\beta)=\cos 90^0 \cos \beta + \sin \beta \sin 90^0=(0)\cos \beta + \sin \beta$ $(1)=,\sin \beta$. Similarly, $\theta+\beta=90^0$, then $\beta=90^0-\theta$. Now, using the sum/difference formula for sine we get answer D. $\sin(90^0-\theta)=\sin 90^0 \cos \theta - \sin \theta \cos 90^0=(1)\cos \theta - \sin \beta$ $(0)=\cos \theta$.
21	C	The correct answer is C. A right triangle can be formed Alex's starting position, his position after he walks down river, and the tree on the other side of the river as shown below. 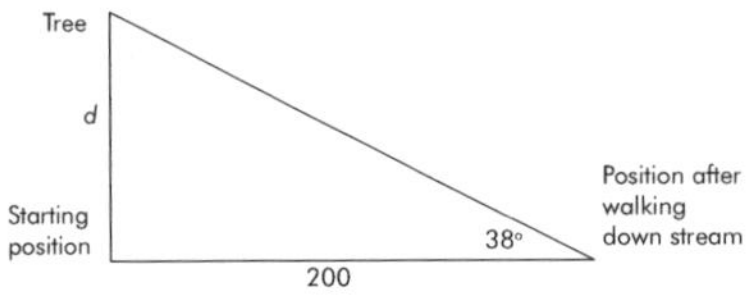 To find the width of the river, we need to find the distance from the starting position to the tree across the river. $\tan 38° = \dfrac{d}{200}$, $d = 200 \tan 38°$, $d = 156$ meters.
22	A	In the diagram below, y is the height of the building. Using the two right triangles, we will set up a system of equations with x, the distance you are after you walk 100 feet, and y. 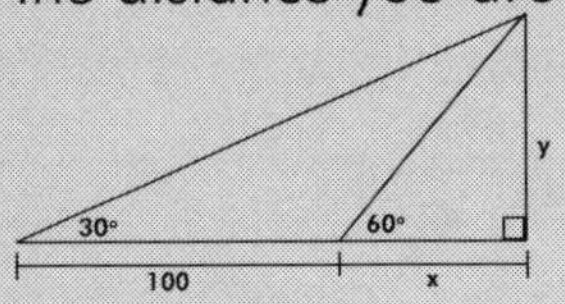 Now, $\tan 60° = \dfrac{y}{x}$ then $x = \dfrac{y}{\tan 60°}$ Also, $\tan 30° = \dfrac{y}{x + 100}$. Solving for x we get, $x = \dfrac{y}{\tan 30°} - 100$. Substituting equation 1 into equation 2 we get, $\dfrac{y}{\tan 60°} = \dfrac{y}{\tan 30°} - 100$. Lastly, solving for y we get, $\dfrac{y}{\tan 60°} = \dfrac{y}{\tan 30°} - 100$, $\dfrac{y}{\sqrt{3}} = \sqrt{3}y - 100$, $\dfrac{y}{\sqrt{3}} - \sqrt{3}y = 100$, $-\dfrac{2}{\sqrt{3}}y = -100$, $Y = 87$.

Question No.	Answer	Detailed Explanation
23	A & C	The correct answers are A and C. Since you must cut squares from each corner of the cardboard before turning those sides up to form the box, you are cutting x inches away twice from both the length and the width of the cardboard as shown in the construction below. 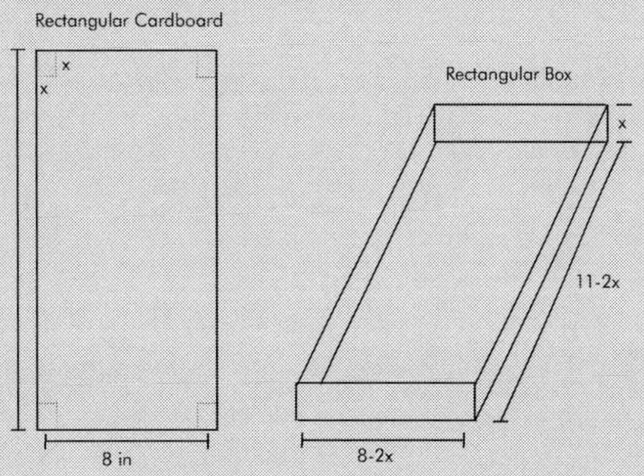 Rectangular Cardboard 11 in 8 in Rectangular Box 11-2x 8-2x
24	A & D	The correct answers are A and D. Answer A may be the more obvious answer since we can form a right triangle with the radius of the cone and the height of the cone which is also equal to the radius as shown in the picture below. 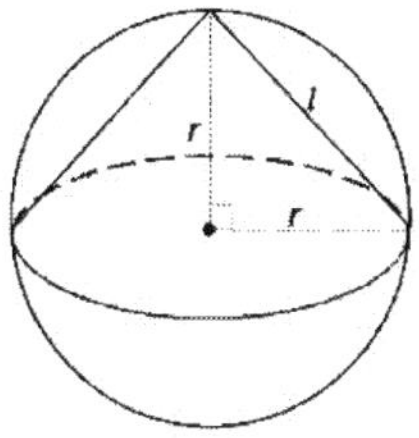 Using the Pythagorean Theorem we get $l^2 = r^2 + r^2$ Answer D is obtained by constructing a perpendicular bisector from the center of the circle to the slant height of the cone. Doing so forms a right triangle with a vertex angle one-half of the central angle of $\pi 2$ whose opposite side is one-half of the slant height and has a hypotenuse of r as shown below. 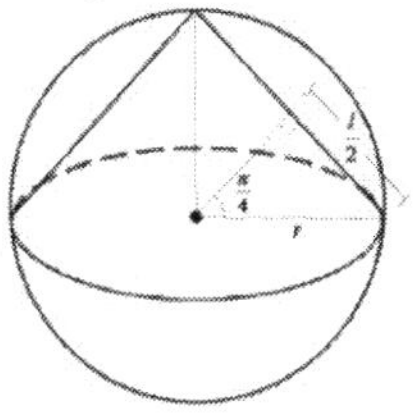 $\sin\frac{\pi}{4} = \frac{\frac{1}{2}}{r}$. Solving for r we get $\sin\frac{\pi}{4} = \frac{\frac{1}{2}}{r}, r\sin\frac{\pi}{4} = r * \frac{\frac{1}{2}}{r}, r\sin\frac{\pi}{4} = \frac{1}{2},$ $2r\sin\frac{\pi}{4} = \frac{1}{2} * 2, l = 2r\sin\frac{\pi}{4}$.

Question No.	Answer	Detailed Explanation
25		The answer is $(x, y) \rightarrow \frac{3}{5}(x+6, y+6)$. The center of circle F translates right 6 units and up 6 units, which is written as $(x, y) \rightarrow (x+6, y+6)$. The radius in the pre-image is 5 and the radius in the post-image is 3. This is a dilation by a factor of $\frac{3}{5}$. The original circle F has its center at the point $(-5, 1)$ with a radius of 5 units. The translated/dilated circle F' has its center at the point $(1, 7)$ with a radius of 3 units. This means the center was translated right 6 units and up 6 units. As a transformation, this translation is written as $(x, y) \rightarrow (x+6, y+6)$. Circle F was also dilated by a factor of $\frac{3}{5}$ because the radius was reduced from 5 units to 3 units. As a transformation, this dilation is written as $(x, y) \rightarrow \frac{3}{5}(x, y)$. Putting the translation and dilation together, the rule is $(x, y) \rightarrow \frac{3}{5}(x+6, y+6)$.
26		The answer is 37°. Inscribed angle $\angle XYZ$ and central angle $\angle ZOX$ form arc $\overset{\frown}{XZ}$, with the same measure as the central angle. Since the measure of an inscribed angle is one-half the measure of its intercepted arc, $m\angle XYZ = 37°$. The circle contains central angle $\angle ZOX$ and $m\angle ZOX = 74°$. A geometry theorem states that the measure of an arc intercepted by a central angle has the same measure as the central angle. Thus, $m \overset{\frown}{XZ} = 74°$. Then, recall the geometry theorem that states that the measure of an inscribed angle is equal to half the measure of its intercepted arc. The inscribed angle, $\angle XYZ$ intercepts $\overset{\frown}{XZ}$. Therefore, $m\angle XYZ = \frac{1}{2}(74°) = 37°$.
27		a) Arc length $= r\theta$; therefore length $= (R)\left(\frac{\pi}{4}\right) = \frac{\pi R}{4}$ b) Arc length $= r\theta$; therefore length $= (2R)\left(\frac{\pi}{4}\right) = \frac{\pi R}{2}$ c) Ratio $= \frac{\pi R/2}{\pi R/4} = 2$

Question No.	Answer	Detailed Explanation
28		The answer is $(x+5)^2+(y+3)^2=72$. The question gives the formula $(x-h)^2+(y-k)^2=r^2$, and since the center is at the point $(-5,-3)$, $h=-5$, and $k=-3$. The distance between the center and the point $(1,3)$ is the radius r. The equation uses r^2, and since the point on the circle is 6 units to the right and 6 units up from the center, $r^2=6^2+6^2=72$. The question asks for the equation in the form $(x-h)^2+(y-k)^2=r^2$. The general form of the point that is the center of a circle is (h, k), so $h=-5$, and $k=-3$. This gives us the equation $(x+5)^2+(y+3)^2=r^2$. The question says if the center of the circle is at the point $(-5,-3)$ and the point $(1, 3)$ is on the circle. This means that the point on the circle is 6 units to the right and 6 units up from the center. Find the radius squared using the Pythagorean Theorem, $x^2+y^2=r^2$, so $r^2=6^2+6^2=72$. The equation of the circle is $(x+5)^2+(y+3)^2=72$.
29		The answer is $y = \frac{1}{4}(x-8)^2 + 4$. Since a parabola is the set of all points in a plane that are equidistant from the focus and the directrix. First, equate those distances: $|y-3| = \sqrt{(x-8)^2 + (y-5)^2}$ Then, square both sides. Simplify and complete the squares to get the equation $4y=(x-8)^2+16$. Finally, solving for y gives the equation $y = \frac{1}{4}(x-8)^2 + 4$. A parabola is defined as the set of all points on a plane that are equidistant from a point called the focus and a line called the directrix as shown in the figure below Let (x, y) be any point on the parabola. Find the distance between the point and the focus: $d = \sqrt{(x-8)^2 + (y-5)^2}$. The distance between the point (x, y) on the parabola and the directrix, $y=3$, is $|y-3|$. Equate the two distances and square both sides. $|y-3| = \sqrt{(x-8)^2 + (y-5)^2}$ Simplify both sides and bring all non $-y$ terms to one side. $(y-3)^2=(x-8)^2+(y-5)^2$. Complete the squares on the right side. $4y=x^2-16x+64+16$ $4y=(x-8)^2+16$ Solve for y: $4y=(x-8)^2+16$ $y = \frac{1}{4}(x-8)^2 + 4$

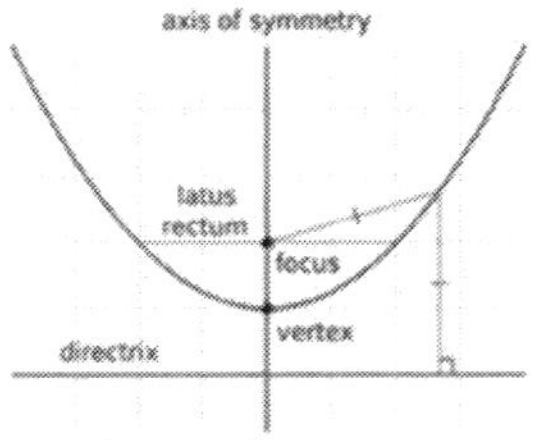

Question No.	Answer	Detailed Explanation
30	C	$$m = \frac{y_2 - y_1}{x_2 - x_1}, [d = \sqrt{(x_2 - x_1)^2 + (y_2 - y_1)^2}]$$ Use the distance formula given above. Plug the values into the formula. Don't forget to square each difference before adding them together. Then find the square root of the value. Be sure to simplify the radical when possible.
31	D	The space left in the can in the difference between the volume of the can and the volume of the sphere according to: $\Delta V = \pi r^2 h - (4/3)\pi r^3$ $\Delta V = \pi(6cm)^2(10cm) - (4/3)\pi(6cm)^3$ $\Delta V = 72\pi cm^3$
32	C	The total volume of the object is the sum of the volumes of the hemisphere and the cone. $V = \frac{1}{2}(4/3)\pi r^3 + (1/3)\pi r^2 h$ $V = \frac{1}{2}(4/3)\pi(3m)^3 + (1/3)\pi(3m)^2(10cm) \, V = 48\pi cm^3$
33		The question gives the sets of letters $U = \{a,b,c,d,e,f,g,h,i,j,k,l,m,n,o,p,q,r,s,t,u,v,w,x,y,z\}$, $A = \{a,e,i,o,u,y\}$, $B = \{a,d,g,j,m,p,s,v,y\}$, and $C = \{a.e.i, m,q,u,y\}$. You are asked to find how many elements is in the set is $\sim A \cup \sim C$. The "$\cap$" symbol means "intersect" which means "in both sets". Thus, the set $\sim A \cap \sim C$ is the set of elements that are in both set $\sim A$ and in set $\sim B$ The set $\sim A = \{b,c,d,f,g,h,j,k,l,m,n,p,q,r,s,t,v,w,x,z\}$. The set $\sim B = \{b,c,e,f,h,i,k,l,n,o,q,r,t,u,w,x,z\}$. Finding the elements in common gives $\sim A \cap \sim B = \{b,c,f,h,k,l,n,q,r,t,w,x,z\}$ Therefore, $\sim A \cup \sim B$ contains 13 elements.
34	C	The probability that event A occurs or that event B occurs is calculated by adding the probability that event A occurs to the probability that event B occurs and then subtracting the probability that events A and B both occur. This probability is calculated by $P(A \text{ or } B) = P(A) + P(B) - P(A \text{ and } B)$. We know that $P(A) = \frac{7}{15}$, $P(B) = \frac{3}{5}$, and $P(A \text{ and } B) = \frac{2}{9}$. Therefore, $P(A) + P(B) - P(A \text{ and } B) = \frac{7}{15} + \frac{3}{5} - \frac{2}{9} = \frac{21}{45} + \frac{27}{45} - \frac{10}{45} = \frac{38}{45}$.

Question No.	Answer	Detailed Explanation
35		Everyone should write down their number. Allowing people to talk to each other could cause them to conspire against one person and also not writing them down allows for someone to change their number mid experiment.
36	B	To determine which bet is a better deal, calculate the expected value of each bet and subtract the cost of the bet. Expected value is the probability of winning the payout times the amount of the payout. Whichever bet has a larger net expected value is the better deal. For Bet A, the expected value is $1/8 * 98 = 12.25$; $12.25 - 10 = 2.25$. For Bet B, the expected value is $4/8 * 24 = 12$; $12 - 8 = 4$. Bet B is the better deal.

Practice Test 2

Question No.	Answer	Detailed Explanation
1		∠FGJ can be found using the information given. From Geometry we know that the exterior angle in a triangle is equal to the sum of its' remote interior angles. ∠FGJ is an exterior angle for ΔEFG. Now we know ∠EFG=80° Since ∠HFG and ∠HFG are supplementary. Next ∠GEF=35° since ∠GEF+∠DEF are supplementary. Therefore ∠FGJ = 35° + 80° = 115°
2		To find the rotational measure, divide 360 (one full rotation) by the number of sides, or angles, the regular polygon has. Equilateral triangle ->**120°** Square -> **90°** Regular pentagon -> **72°** Regular hexagon -> **60°**
3	C	A rotation turns the figure. Although B is congruent, it is not due to a rotation of 180 degrees.
4	B	The postulate that is being stated is referring to two angles and the side that is between them, or the angle-side-angle postulate.
5	Jack	The angles are corresponding angles and therefore are congruent so the measure of angle X is 56 degrees.
6		An isosceles triangle must have two angles that are congruent. However, the third angle must be 65 degrees because all three of the angles must add to 180 degrees. Therefor Henry is correct.
7	A	The question states that the given elliptical figure is translated up 5 units and to the right 5 units. A translation is a sliding movement. The figure does not change size, shape, or orientation. Therefore, the pre-image and the post-image are congruent.
8	D	A rigid motion maps the pre-image onto the post-image without changing the size or shape of the object. In the two triangles, the following sides are corresponding and their lengths are provided: AB = 5 and A'B' = 6; BC = 7, AC = 6 and A'C' = 5. Since corresponding sides are not congruent, the transformation is not a rigid motion.

Question No.	Answer	Detailed Explanation
9	D	A rigid motion maintains the original size and shape of the pre-image. Thus, the post-image is congruent to the pre-image. If the transformation ΔABC → ΔDEC represents a rigid motion, then ΔABC ≅ ΔDEC From the figure we can see that ∠A ≅ ∠D and AB ≅ DE. We can also say ∠ACB ≅ ∠DCE because they are vertical angles. The two triangles are congruent by the AAS triangle congruence method, thus validating that ΔABC → ΔDEC represents some type of rigid motion.
10	C	The question states that, in the figure, m∠2 = m∠6, m∠1 = m∠5. These angles are pairs of corresponding angles. If corresponding angles are congruent, then the lines are parallel.
11	C	The question does not provide any information about the length of the sides of the two triangles, but the question states that m∠4= m∠6; m∠1= m∠3; m∠4 = m∠5; ∠DEB ≅ ∠DCB. Since m∠4= m∠6, ∠4 ≅ ∠6, AD ≅ BD because of isosceles triangle properties. This information indicates that at least two corresponding angles in the two triangles are congruent and the ratio of the sides is 1.1. Thus, by the ASA triangle congruence theorem, we can state that the triangles are congruent: ΔBDE ≅ ΔBAD.
12	B	The input variable is x. Squaring the input variable is a term x^2. Tripling that value is a term $3x^2$. Adding five times the input variable is the term $+5x$. Subtracting twelve is the term -12. Out together, we have $f(x)=3x^2+5x-12$.
13	B	The parabolic path is that of a parabola opening upward. Thus, the vertex (4, 1) contains the minimum value of the parabolic function. The vertex occurs at 4 seconds because the x-axis represents time. The minimum height is 100 feet because the y-scale is marked at x100 feet.
14	C	A function is decreasing when its rate of change is negative. This usually occurs between a local maximum point and a local minimum point. The function f(x) has a local maximum at (-0.43, 1.23) and a local minimum at (3.10, -4.26) with a negative rate of change between these two points.
15	C	The correct answer is C. The expression 1.75x+2.25y will give the combined profit the company will obtain selling x cartons of grape soda and y cartons of cherry soda which is not a constraint for the graph. x+y≤1500 is the inequality for the first constraint. y≤½x is the inequality for the second constraint and x≤500+2y is the inequality for the third constraint.

Question No.	Answer	Detailed Explanation
16		It is possible to disprove your friends conjecture. While it is not shown as a step in his proof, your friend divided step 5 by (a -- b) to get to step 6. Since he assumed a = b in step one, then (a -- b) must have a value of zero. Since we cannot divide by zero, you invalidate your friends assumption that a = b
17	C	Each of the side lengths of ΔDEF are twice as long as the ΔABC, therefore the scale factor is 2.
18	B	Answer is B. The definition of scale factor is given in the question.
19	C	Answer is C. The original line segment has a length of 2 units. If the scale factor of the new image is s, the new line segment must have a length of 4.
20	D	A dilation of 0.5 will shrink the original image in half. D is the only with smaller than the preimage.
21	B	In order for triangles to be similar, the angle measures need to be the same. Since 56 degrees is not congruent to the measure of angle B it is not similar.
22		For a) and b): scale factor = 1/2 scale factor = 2 c) A scale factor < 1 results in a reduction in the size of the image. A scale factor > 1 results in an enlargement of the image. a) and b) When a dilation is performed about the origin, the image points may be found by multiplying the x and y coordinates by the scale factor. When the scale factor is 2, A' = 2*(-2,2) = (-4,4), B' = 2*(2,2) = (4,4), C' = 2*(2,-2) = (4,-4), D' = 2*(-2,-2) = (-4,-4).When the scale factor is ½, A' = ½ (-2,2) = (-1,1), B' = ½ (2,2) = (1,1), C' = ½ (2,-2) = (1,-1),D' = ½ (-2,-2) = (-1,-1).

Question No.	Answer	Detailed Explanation
23	B	Since the sum of the angles in a triangle must be 180°, we can find the missing angles in each triangle. $\angle E=25°$ and $\angle A=65°$. If at least two angles in the triangles are congruent, the triangles are similar by AA Postulate. This situation is now known to be true. When writing the similarity statements, the congruent angles must be in the corresponding position in the triangle names. $\angle A$ and $\angle D$ are both 65° so they must correspond. $\angle B$ and $\angle Q$ are both 90° so they must correspond.
24	D	When writing the similarity statements, the congruent angles must be in the corresponding position in the triangle names. So $\angle MLN$ and $\angle MXY$ are both 65° so they must correspond. $\angle M$ and $\angle M$ are congruent by the Reflexive Property so they must correspond.
25	C	Circle A and circle B are similar when circle A can be translated and dilated to produce circle B. The dilation of 3/2 was given in the problem statement. Circle A must be moved 9 units to the right and 3 units downward in order to align with the center of circle B. Therefore $x' = x + 9$ and $y' = y - 3$.
26		a) Arc length $= r\theta$; therefore length $= (R)(\frac{\pi}{4})=\frac{\pi R}{4}$ b) Arc length $= r\theta$; therefore length $= (2R)(\frac{\pi}{4})=\frac{\pi R}{2}$ c) Ratio $= \dfrac{\pi R/2}{\pi R/4} = 2$
27		**12 cm:** Arc length $= r\theta$; therefore length $= (12cm)(\frac{\pi}{4})=3\pi$ cm Area $= \dfrac{\theta}{2\pi}\pi r^2 = \dfrac{\theta}{2}r^2$; therefore Area $= \dfrac{\pi/4}{2}(12\text{ cm})^2 = 18\pi \text{cm}^2$ **5 cm:** Arc length$=r\theta$; therefore $\theta=$length/r; $\theta=(\dfrac{10\pi/3cm}{5\text{ cm}})=\dfrac{2\pi}{3}$ Area $= \dfrac{\theta}{2\pi}\pi r^2 = \dfrac{\theta}{2}r^2$; therefore Area $= \dfrac{2\pi/3}{2}(5\text{ cm})^2=\dfrac{25\pi}{3}\text{cm}^2$

Question No.	Answer	Detailed Explanation
28		The answer is yes. First, find the radius of the circle using the distance formula from the center to the point on the circle: $r=\sqrt{(-5-2)^2+(-8+32)^2}=25$. Next, used the distance formula again to find the distance from the center to the point $(2,6)$: $r=\sqrt{(-5-2)^2+(-8-16)^2}=25$. Since the distances are the same, the point is on the circle. The equation of a circle is in the form $(x-h)^2+(y-k)^2=r^2$. The general form of the point that is the center of a circle is (h,k), so $h=-5$, and $k=-8$. This gives us the equation $(x+5)^2+(y+8)^2=r^2$. The question says the circle contains the point $(2,-32)$. This means that the radius of the circle is the distance between the points $(-5,-8)$ and $(2,-32)$. Use the distance formula to find the radius squared. $r=\sqrt{(-5-2)^2+(-8+32)^2}=25$, so $r^2=625$. The equation of the circle is $(x+5)^2+(y+8)^2=625$. Now, substitute the point into the equation for x and y. If the result is a true statement, then the point is on the circle. $(2,16):(-5-2)^2+(-8-16)^2=625$; $49+576=625$; the point is on the circle.
29		If two lines are parallel, they have the same slope. The slope-intercept form of a linear equation is $y=mx+b$, where m is the slope and b is the y-intercept. The slope of the given equation $y=-5x+3$ is -5. Since the questions asks for a line that is parallel to the given line, the answer is a line with the same slope. The question gives a point the new line must pass through, and the given equation gives the slope, so use the point-slope form of the equation to find an equation of the line. The point-slope equation of a line is $y-y_1=m(x-x_1)$, where x and y are the variables in the equation and (x_1,y_1) is the point the line passes through. Thus, the point-slope equation is $y-7=-5(x-4)$. The standard form is $Ax+By=C$, where A, B, and C are constants. Change the equation above to the standard form by distributing to remove the parenthesis: $y-7=-5(x-4)$; $y-7=-5x+20$ The by adding or subtracting terms from both sides. Ensure the leading coefficient is positive. $y-7=-5x+20$; $5x+y=20+7$; $5x+y=27$

Question No.	Answer	Detailed Explanation
30	B	$(\dfrac{x_1+x_2}{2}, \dfrac{y_1+y_2}{2})$ Midpoint Formula Here, $x_1 = 1$, $x_2 = 4$ and $y_1 = -3$, $y_2 = 2$ Substituting these values in the formula, we get, $(\dfrac{1+4}{2}, \dfrac{-3+2}{2}) = \dfrac{5}{2}, \dfrac{-1}{2}$ Hence, B is the correct answer choice.
31		Visualize the cylinder that would be formed. 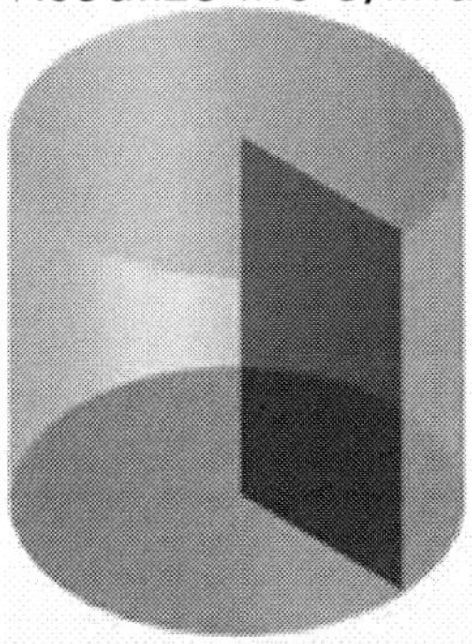 The height of the cylinder will be equal to the length of the rectangle. The radius of the cylinder will be equal to the width of the rectangle. Therefore: $V = \pi r^2 h = \pi(2)^2(10) = \pi(4)(10) = 40\pi$ units^3
32		A triangular cross section is formed when a cone is sliced down its center. A rectangular cross section is formed when a cylinder is sliced down its center. A circular cross section is formed when a sphere is sliced down its center.
33		The sample space of the result of tossing three coins is shown below. 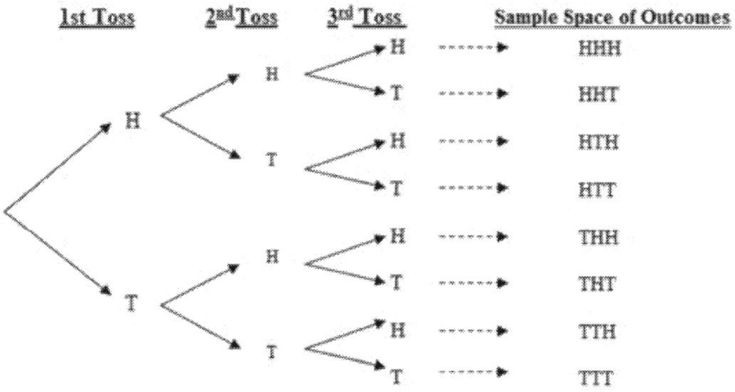 Notice that the outcomes of the third toss are always heads or tails. Thus, no matter what the first two tosses give, the third toss will result in either heads or tails. Thus, the results of the first two tosses do not affect the result of the third toss. Thus, the probability of throwing a head in the third toss is ½.

Question No.	Answer	Detailed Explanation
34	A	The report shows that in a high school with 400 students, there are 40% girls. The report says that 20% of the students in the school wear glasses. It is also known that 10% of the boys wear glasses. We are asked to determine how many boys wear glasses. If 40% of the students at the school are girls, then 60% are boys. This means there are $400 \times 60\% = 240$ boys in the school. Then, since 10% of the boys wear glasses, $240 \times 10\% = 24$ boys wear glasses.
35		Incorrect, the chances are actually 100% based on this wording. If you read the question carefully it says ``the chances that the item will be bought by a random person or not be bought by a random person". They are definitely going to be bought...or not bought...so the chances of this scenario are 100%.
36	C	A die has six numbers, 1,2,3,4,5,6. Three numbers are odd: 1,3,5. Three numbers are even: 2,4,6. Since the number of odd numbers and the number of even numbers are the same, each team has the same number of chances to bat first. Therefore, the method is fair.

Chapter 1 - Congruence

1. Select the best word to fill in the blank in this sentence: In geometry, all figures consist of

   Ⓐ lines
   Ⓑ angles
   Ⓒ points
   Ⓓ circles

2. Select the best word to fill in the blank in this sentence: In geometry, a line is defined as a set of points on a plane that extend in two directions without _____.

   Ⓐ curving
   Ⓑ ending
   Ⓒ bending
   Ⓓ moving

3. What are the coordinates of point A' if point A in the figure below is translated 5 units down?

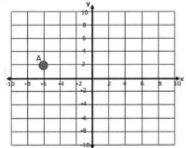

   Ⓐ (-6,-2)
   Ⓑ (-6,-3)
   Ⓒ (-3,-6)
   Ⓓ (-2,-3)

4. **What are the coordinates of point A' if point in the figure below is reflected across the y-axis?**

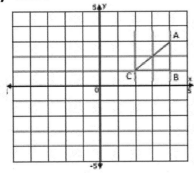

Ⓐ (4, -3)
Ⓑ (-4, -3)
Ⓒ (-3, -4)
Ⓓ (-4, 3)

5. **Suppose ABCD identify as a quadrilateral is reflected across the y-axis and then across the x-axis. Which translation will translate the rectangle back to its original location?**

Ⓐ Reflection across the x-axis
Ⓑ Reflection across the y-axis
Ⓒ Reflection across the origin
Ⓓ Reflection across the line

6. **What is the translation rule that translates the triangle in the graph on the left to the triangle in the graph on the right?**

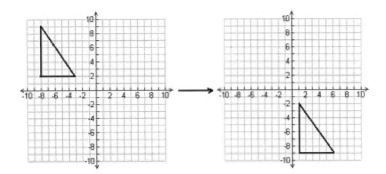

Ⓐ (x, y) → (x-9, y+11)
Ⓑ (x, y) → (x+9, y-11)
Ⓒ (x, y) → (x+9, y+11)
Ⓓ (x, y) → (x-9, y-11)

7. Which figure shows polygon ABCDE reflected over side AE?

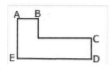

Ⓐ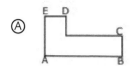

Ⓒ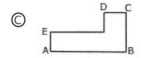

Ⓑ

Ⓓ

8. Which figure shows quadrilateral ABCD rotated 30⁰ about vertex C clockwise?

Ⓐ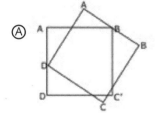

Ⓒ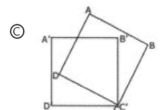

Ⓑ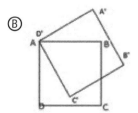

Ⓓ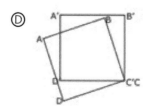

9. A polygon, ABCD with the coordinates of (2, 0), (1, 2), (-1, 1), and (0, -2) respectively is transformed first by reflecting over the x-axis and then translated two units to the right and one unit up. What would be the coordinate of B' ?

   Ⓐ (1, -2)
   Ⓑ (1, 0)
   Ⓒ (2, 3)
   Ⓓ (3, -1)

10. What combination of transformations will map the polygon ABCD onto A'B'C'D' ?

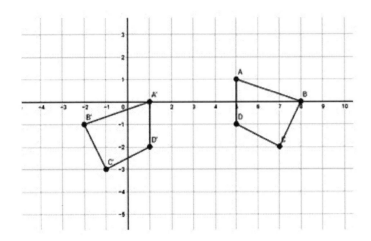

   Ⓐ A reflection over the line x = 3 and a rotation of 90 degrees counterclockwise about the center
   Ⓑ A translation of two units to the left and one unit down and reflection over the line x = 2
   Ⓒ A rotation of 180 degrees about the point (3, 0)
   Ⓓ A reflection over the x-axis and a translation of two units to the left and one unit up.

11. Which of the following combinations of transformations will create an image that is congruent to the original?

   Ⓐ A reflection over the origin and a vertical stretch
   Ⓑ A rotation of 45 degrees clockwise and a reflection over the y-axis
   Ⓒ A dilation of 0.5 and a translation of four units down
   Ⓓ A reflection across the line x = 4 and a horizontal stretch

12. Which of the following transformations of the circle, shown below, result in a congruent circle?

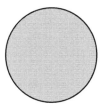

I – translation; II – rotation; III – reflection; IV - dilation

Ⓐ I, II, IV
Ⓑ I, III, IV
Ⓒ I, II, III
Ⓓ All of them

13. A ladder is leaning up against a wall to reach a window creating a triangle with the building and the ground. If the ladder is moved seven feet to the next window on the same level creating another triangle. Is the new triangle congruent to the original triangle?

Ⓐ No they are not congruent since it is a reflection
Ⓑ No they are not congruent since it is a translation
Ⓒ Yes they are congruent since it is a reflection
Ⓓ Yes they are congruent since it is a translation

14. A ladder is leaning up against the side of a building forming a triangle. The ladder is extended to reach further up the building forming another triangle. Are the two triangles congruent?

Ⓐ No they are not congruent since it is a translation
Ⓑ No they are not congruent since it is a dilation
Ⓒ Yes they are congruent since it is a translation
Ⓓ Yes they are congruent since it is a dilation

15. Which of the following is needed in order to determine if two triangles are congruent?

Ⓐ Any two angles that are congruent
Ⓑ Two angles and a side that are congruent
Ⓒ Two sides that are congruent and the congruent angle that is in between the two sides
Ⓓ Two sides that are congruent and an angle that is congruent

16. Which triangle congruence method can we use to say that ΔABC → ΔDCB represents some type of rigid motion?

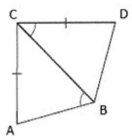

Ⓐ ASA
Ⓑ SSS
Ⓒ SAS
Ⓓ The Δ's are not necessarily congruent

17. Which of the following is not a way to prove that lines are parallel?

Ⓐ Prove corresponding angles are congruent
Ⓑ Prove alternate interior angles are congruent
Ⓒ Prove angles on the same side of a transversal are supplementary
Ⓓ Prove the lines are perpendicular to a third line

18. Given: m∠4=m∠6; m∠1=m∠3; ∠DEB ≅ ∠DCB. What can we say about ΔBED and ΔBAD?

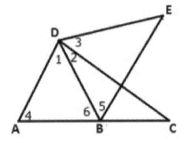

Ⓐ ΔBED : ΔBAD
Ⓑ ΔBED : ΔABD
Ⓒ ΔBDE ≅ ΔBAD
Ⓓ ΔBED : ΔBDA

19. Quadrilateral ABCD is a parallelogram. What is the length of BD ?

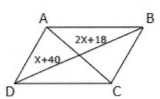

Ⓐ 22
Ⓑ 62
Ⓒ 44
Ⓓ 124

20. Which of the following is a square inscribed in a circle?

Ⓐ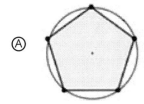

Ⓑ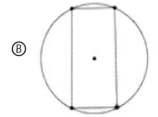

Ⓒ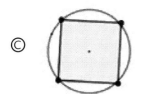

Ⓓ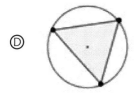

Chapter 2 - Similarity, Right Triangles, and Trigonometry

1. Perform a dilation on point A centered at the origin with scale factor equal to 2. What is the coordinate of the resulting image point A'?

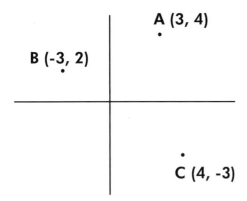

Ⓐ (8 , 6)
Ⓑ (6 , 8)
Ⓒ (3/2 , 2)
Ⓓ (2 , 3/2)

2. Perform a dilation on point B centered at the origin with scale factor equal to 3. What is the coordinate of the resulting image point B'?

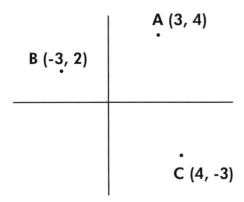

Ⓐ (-1 , 2/3)
Ⓑ (2/3 , -1)
Ⓒ (-9 , 6)
Ⓓ (6 , -9)

3. Perform a dilation on point C centered at the origin with scale factor equal to 1/2. What is the coordinate of the resulting image point C'?

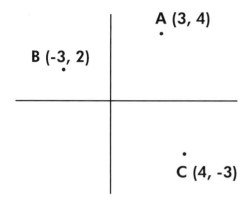

A (3, 4)

B (-3, 2)

C (4, -3)

Ⓐ (2 , -3/2)
Ⓑ (-3/2 , 2)
Ⓒ (8 , -6)
Ⓓ (-6 , 8)

4. The triangles in the diagram below are similar. Find the value of x.
   Note: Round to the nearest tenth.

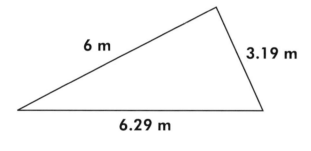

6 m   3.19 m

6.29 m

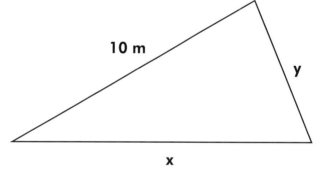

10 m   y

x

Ⓐ 4.67m
Ⓑ 7.00m
Ⓒ 10.5m
Ⓓ 15.8m

5. The triangles in the diagram below are similar. Find the value of y.
Note: Round to the nearest tenth.

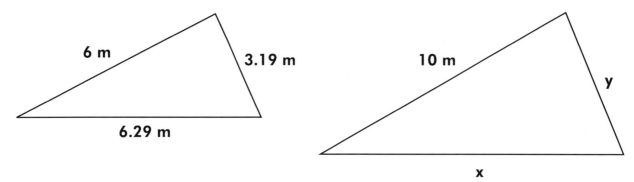

- Ⓐ 4.26m
- Ⓑ 5.32m
- Ⓒ 6.65m
- Ⓓ 8.31m

6. ΔABC and ΔDEF in the diagram below are similar. Find the value of x.

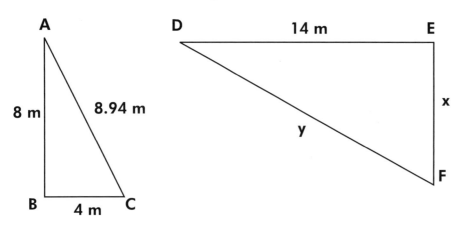

- Ⓐ 3.58m
- Ⓑ 4.48m
- Ⓒ 5.60m
- Ⓓ 7.00m

7. Use the diagram below. Given that ∠K ≅ ∠B, what additional statement will prove that ΔABC ~ ΔJKC?

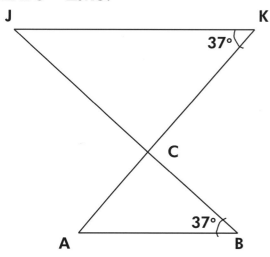

Ⓐ ∠ABC ≅ ∠JKC because vertical angles are congruent

Ⓑ ∠ACB ≅ ∠KCJ by the Reflexive Property

Ⓒ ∠KJC ≅ ∠BAC because they are right angles

Ⓓ ∠KJC ≅ ∠BAC because alternate interior angles are congruent

8. Use the diagram below. Given that ∠XQW ≅ ∠YQZ which additional statement shows that ΔQXW ≅ ΔQZY?

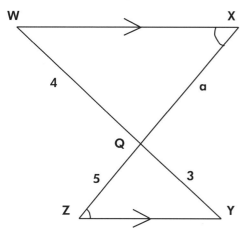

Ⓐ ∠X ≅ ∠Z because parallel lines cut by a transversal form the corresponding angles which are congruent

Ⓑ ∠X ≅ ∠Z because parallel lines cut by a transversal form same side interior angles which are supplementary

Ⓒ ∠X ≅ ∠Z and ∠W ≅ ∠Y because parallel lines cut by a transversal, then the alternate interior angles formed are congruent

Ⓓ ∠X ≅ ∠Z because parallel lines cut by a transversal form alternate exterior angles which are congruent

LumosLearning.com

9. Use the diagram below. Find a.

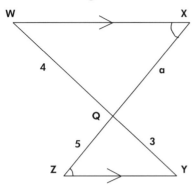

Ⓐ $\dfrac{15}{4}$

Ⓑ $\dfrac{20}{3}$

Ⓒ $\dfrac{12}{5}$

Ⓓ 6

10. Given that ΔABC is a right triangle in which the hypotenuse is $\overline{AC}$, if AB = 3 and BC = 4, what is AC?

Ⓐ 5
Ⓑ 25
Ⓒ $\sqrt{34}$
Ⓓ $\sqrt{41}$

11. ΔABC has $\overline{RS}$ drawn parallel to side BC in such a way that $\overline{RS}$ cuts $\overline{AB}$ into AR = 5 and RB = 8. $\overline{AC}$ is cut into AS = x and SC = 6. Find the value of x.

Ⓐ 3.75
Ⓑ 9.6
Ⓒ 10
Ⓓ 3.33

12. ΔZXA has $\overline{YB}$ drawn parallel to side XA in such a way that $\overline{YB}$ cuts $\overline{ZX}$ into ZY = 6 and YX = 7. $\overline{ZA}$ is cut into ZB = x and BA = 14. Find the value of x.

Ⓐ 16.3
Ⓑ 6.5
Ⓒ 12
Ⓓ 9.2

13. Given that ΔABC ≅ ΔEFG, E=30°, B=124°, what is the measure of ∠C?

Ⓐ **26°**
Ⓑ **30°**
Ⓒ **56°**
Ⓓ **150°**

14. Given that ΔGHI ≅ ΔRST, which side is congruent to $\overline{GI}$?

Ⓐ $\overline{HI}$
Ⓑ $\overline{RS}$
Ⓒ $\overline{RT}$
Ⓓ $\overline{ST}$

15. What is the triangle similarity statement for the two triangles?

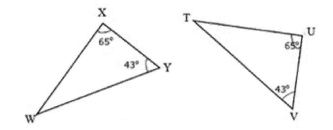

Ⓐ **ΔWXY~ΔUVT**
Ⓑ **ΔWXY~ΔTUV**
Ⓒ **ΔWYX~ΔTUV**
Ⓓ **They are not similar**

16. What is the triangle similarity statement for the two triangles?

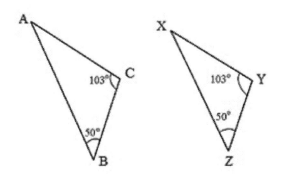

Ⓐ **ΔABC~ΔXYZ**
Ⓑ **ΔABC~ΔXZY**
Ⓒ **They are not similar**
Ⓓ **ΔABC~ΔZYX**

17. In the figure below, ΔPQR is a right triangle. Which trigonometric ratio is equivalent to cos P?

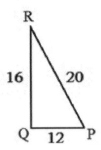

Ⓐ cos R
Ⓑ tan R
Ⓒ sin R
Ⓓ sin Q

18. In the figure below, ΔKJL is a right triangle. Which trigonometric ratio is equivalent to cos K?

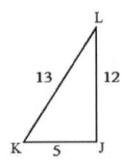

Ⓐ cos L
Ⓑ tan J
Ⓒ sin L
Ⓓ sin K

19. Suppose that just after midday, a building casts a shadow that is 11 feet long. The distance from the top of the building to the end of the shadow is 61 feet. How tall is the building?

Ⓐ 58 feet
Ⓑ 60 feet
Ⓒ 54 feet
Ⓓ 59 feet

20. What is the length of the hypotenuse of a right triangle if the lengths of the sides are 8 and 15?

Ⓐ 17
Ⓑ 23
Ⓒ 12.68
Ⓓ 18.4

Chapter 3 - Circles

1. Given the radius of a circle is $r_1=4$ cm, and the radius of a second circle is $r_2=2$ cm, find the ratio of the diameters of the circles, $\left(\frac{d_1}{d_2}\right)$.

   Ⓐ 1
   Ⓑ 2
   Ⓒ 4
   Ⓓ 8

2. Given the radius of a circle is $r_1 = 8$ cm, and the radius of a second circle is $r_2=2$ cm, find the ratio of the circumferences of the circles, $\left(\frac{C_1}{C_2}\right)$.

   Ⓐ 2
   Ⓑ π
   Ⓒ 4
   Ⓓ 8

3. Given the diameter of a circle is $d_1 = 20$ cm, and the diameter of a second circle is $d_2=4$ cm, find the ratio of the circumferences of the circles, $\left(\frac{C_1}{C_2}\right)$

   Ⓐ π
   Ⓑ 5
   Ⓒ 5π
   Ⓓ 25

4. Given the radius of a circle is $r_1 = 15$ cm, and the radius of a second circle is $r_2 = 3$ cm, find the ratio of the areas of the circles, $\left(\frac{A_1}{A_2}\right)$.

   Ⓐ 5
   Ⓑ 5π
   Ⓒ 25
   Ⓓ 25π

5. What is the translation rule and the scale factor of the dilation as Circle F → Circle F'.

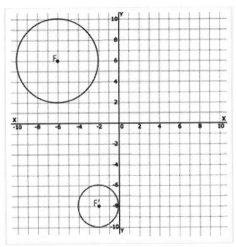

Ⓐ (x,y)→2(x+4,y−14)
Ⓑ (x,y)→½(x+4,y−14)
Ⓒ (x,y)→½(x−4,y+14)
Ⓓ (x,y)→½(x+14,y−4)

6. Given the circle in the figure shown below with m∠ABC=120° where point B is located at the center of the circle, find the measure of ∠ADC.

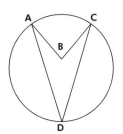

Ⓐ 30°
Ⓑ 60°
Ⓒ 80°
Ⓓ 120°

7. In the circle shown in the figure below, m∠ABC=80°. Point B is located at the center of the circle, and line segment BD bisects ∠ADC. Find m∠BCD.

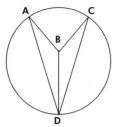

Ⓐ 20°
Ⓑ 40°
Ⓒ 60°
Ⓓ 80°

8. Quadrilateral ABCD is inscribed in circle O, as shown in the figure below. What is m∠DAB?

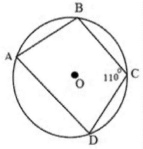

Ⓐ 60°
Ⓑ 70°
Ⓒ 80°
Ⓓ 82°

9. The figure below shows circle O, with segment OB and chord AC. What is the value of x?

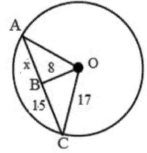

Ⓐ 14
Ⓑ 15
Ⓒ 15.5
Ⓓ 16

10. **The figure below shows circle O. The segment OC contains the center of the circle, point O, and chord AB. What is the value of x?**

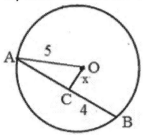

Ⓐ 2
Ⓑ 3
Ⓒ 4
Ⓓ 5

11. **m∠A=80°, ∠B=70°, ∠C=30° Determine m∠DAO.**

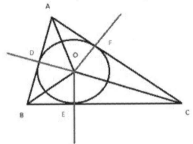

Ⓐ 10°
Ⓑ 20°
Ⓒ 40°
Ⓓ 80°

12. **Circle O circumscribes ΔABC.**
    m∠BFO=90°
    OF is perpendicular to FB.
    Determine the length of AF.

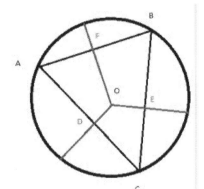

Ⓐ 4 cm
Ⓑ 6 cm
Ⓒ 8 cm
Ⓓ 12 cm

13. m∠A=100°. Determine m∠C.

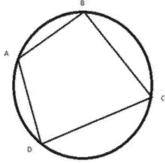

Ⓐ **20°**
Ⓑ **40°**
Ⓒ **60°**
Ⓓ **80°**

14. A circle is inscribed inside ΔXYZ with tangent points U, V, and W. What is the length of segment XY?

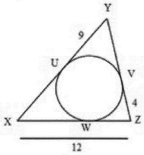

Ⓐ **17**
Ⓑ **12**
Ⓒ **13**
Ⓓ **18**

15. A circle is inscribed inside ΔABC with tangent points X, Y, and Z. What is the length of segment BC?

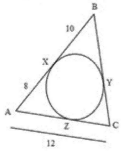

Ⓐ **17**
Ⓑ **14**
Ⓒ **12**
Ⓓ **18**

16. Calculate the length of an arc of radius 12 ft intercepted by an angle $\theta=\frac{7}{4}\pi$.

Ⓐ $\frac{21}{2}$ πft

Ⓑ 21 πft

Ⓒ 32π

Ⓓ 42π

17. Calculate the length of an arc of radius 18 ft intercepted by an angle $\theta=\frac{2\pi}{3}$.

Ⓐ 3πft

Ⓑ 6πft

Ⓒ 12πft

Ⓓ 24πft

18. Calculate the area of a sector of radius 6 cm and arc $\theta=\frac{\pi}{3}$.

Ⓐ 3πcm²

Ⓑ 6πcm²

Ⓒ 9πcm²

Ⓓ 18πcm²

19. What is the approximate area of the sector of the circle that is shaded? Use π=3.14 in your calculations.

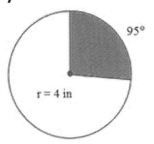

Ⓐ 13.258 in

Ⓑ 4.222 in²

Ⓒ 13.258 in²

Ⓓ $\frac{38}{9}$π in²

20. What is the exact length of the arc subtended by the sector of the circle that is shaded?

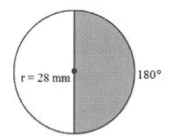

Ⓐ **28π mm²**
Ⓑ **28 mm**
Ⓒ **87.92 mm**
Ⓓ **28π mm**

Chapter 4 - Expressing Geometric Properties with Equations

1. Find the equation of the circle that has center at (3, -4) and radius = 11.

   Ⓐ $(x-3)^2+(y+4)^2=121$
   Ⓑ $(x-3)^2+(y-4)^2=121$
   Ⓒ $(x+3)^2+(y-4)^2=121$
   Ⓓ $(x-3)^2+(y+4)^2=11$

2. If a circle has an equation of $(x+1)^2+(y-7)^2=23$, what are the coordinates of the center and the value of the radius?

   Ⓐ $C(1, -7); r=\sqrt{23}$
   Ⓑ $C(1, 49); r=23$
   Ⓒ $C(-1, 7); r=\sqrt{23}$
   Ⓓ $C(-1, 7); r=23$

3. Find the correct transformation of the circle whose equation is $(x-2)^2+(y+3)^2=16$.

   Ⓐ left two, up 3; r = 4
   Ⓑ left two, up 3; r = 16
   Ⓒ right two, down 3, r = 16
   Ⓓ right two, down 3; r = 4

4. The graph of $x^2+y^2=49$ is translated 12 units left and 9 units down. What is the equation of the new circle?

   Ⓐ $(x-12)^2+(y-9)^2=49$
   Ⓑ $(x+6)^2+(y+3)^2=49$
   Ⓒ $(x+12)^2+(y+9)^2=49$
   Ⓓ $(x-6)^2+(y-3)^2=49$

5. A four-sided figure has vertices at R(3, 5), S(7, 6), T(2, 1), and U(6, 2). Determine the most exact name for the figure.

   Ⓐ Quadrilateral
   Ⓑ Square
   Ⓒ Rhombus
   Ⓓ Rectangle

6. Find the equation of a circle that contains the point (2, 7) and whose center is located at (-1, 4).

    Ⓐ $(x-1)^2+(y+4)^2=\sqrt{32}$
    Ⓑ $(x+1)^2+(y-4)^2=18$
    Ⓒ $(x+1)^2+(y-4)^2=\sqrt{32}$
    Ⓓ $(x-1)^2+(y+4)^2=18$

7. A circle has its center at the point (−3, 8) and passes through the point (4, 3). Which one of the following points lies on the circle?

    Ⓐ (2, 15)
    Ⓑ (−10, 12)
    Ⓒ (3, 14)
    Ⓓ (−9, 15)

8. A circle has its center at the point (−4, −5) and passes through the point (4, 10). Which one of the following points lies on the circle?

    Ⓐ (5, 9)
    Ⓑ (−9, −15)
    Ⓒ (−11, −19)
    Ⓓ (−12, −20)

9. Line *j* passes through the points (2, -3) and (5, 1). Line k passes through the points (-5,2) and (3,7). Describe the relationship between the lines.

    Ⓐ Parallel because their slopes are the same
    Ⓑ Parallel because their slopes are negative reciprocals
    Ⓒ Perpendicular because their slopes are negative reciprocals
    Ⓓ Neither parallel nor perpendicular

10. What is the equation of a line in Standard form containing the points (-6, -2) and (-3, 8).

    Ⓐ 10x - 3y = -54
    Ⓑ 2x + 3y = 18
    Ⓒ 2x + y = 2
    Ⓓ 10x + 9x = 42

11. **What is the equation, in point-slope form, of the line that passes through the point (2,−4), and is parallel to the line with the equation y=6x-1?**

    Ⓐ $y-4=6(x-2)$
    Ⓑ $y+4=-\dfrac{1}{6}(x-2)$
    Ⓒ $y-4=6(x+2)$
    Ⓓ $y+4=6(x-2)$

12. **What is the equation, in point-slope form, of the line that passes through the point (4,−8), and is perpendicular to the line with the equation y=x-9?**

    Ⓐ $y-8=(x-4)$
    Ⓑ $y-8=-(x+4)$
    Ⓒ $y+8=-(x-4)$
    Ⓓ $y-8=(x+4)$

13. **A directed line segment is a line segment from one point to another point in the coordinate plane. When using directed line segments, pay close attention to the beginning and endpoints of the line.**

    Point M is the midpoint of $\overline{CD}$. If CM = 4x-1 and DM = 2x+7, what is the length of $\overline{CD}$?

    Ⓐ 30
    Ⓑ 15
    Ⓒ 22
    Ⓓ 11

14. **Point R is the midpoint of $\overline{JK}$ and $\overline{AB}$. The coordinates of J, K, and A are J(-4, 5), K(6, -5), A(2, 8). What are the coordinates of point B?**

    Ⓐ $(\dfrac{3}{2},4)$
    Ⓑ $(\dfrac{1}{2},\dfrac{7}{2})$
    Ⓒ $(-2, -6)$
    Ⓓ $(0, -8)$

15. **What value on the number line in the figure below divides segment CD into two parts having a ratio of their lengths of 1:2?**

    Ⓐ -20
    Ⓑ 10
    Ⓒ -10
    Ⓓ -5

16. **What value on the number line in the figure below divides segment OP into two parts having a ratio of their lengths of 7:2?**

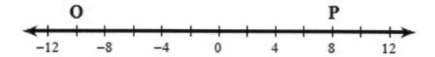

Ⓐ -6
Ⓑ -4
Ⓒ 0
Ⓓ 4

17. **What coordinate of vertex, R, would produce a rhombus if the other three vertices of the rhombus are P(3, 4), Q(-1, 1), and S(6, 8)?**

Ⓐ R (0, 7)
Ⓑ R (1, -3)
Ⓒ R (5, 1)
Ⓓ R (2, 5)

18. **The vertices of a rhombus are A(2, 5), B(-1, 1), C(3,4) and D(6, 8). Find the perimeter of the rhombus.**

Ⓐ 80
Ⓑ 100
Ⓒ 20
Ⓓ 28

19. What is the perimeter of polygon ABC in the figure below?

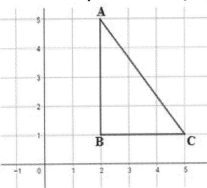

Ⓐ 10
Ⓑ 11
Ⓒ 12
Ⓓ 13

20. What is the perimeter of polygon XYZ in the figure below?

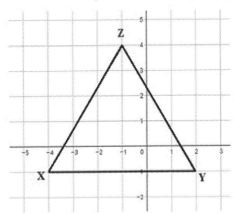

Ⓐ $6+\sqrt{234}$
Ⓑ $6+\sqrt{34}$
Ⓒ $8+\sqrt{34}$
Ⓓ $8\sqrt{34}$

1. A ball with radius 6 cm just fits inside a cylindrical can with radius of 6 cm and height 10 cm. How much empty space is left in the can?

   Ⓐ 18π cm³
   Ⓑ 36π cm³
   Ⓒ 54π cm³
   Ⓓ 72π cm³

2. A cone of radius r and height h is placed inside a cylindrical can of radius r and height h. What fraction of the available volume does the cone occupy?

   Ⓐ 1/9
   Ⓑ 1/6
   Ⓒ 1/3
   Ⓓ 1/2

3. A hopper for storing grain is built in the shape of an inverted pyramid with a square base of edge width 5 m. The full height of the pyramid is 15 m; however, the bottom 3 m was removed to provide a means to empty the hopper. Find the volume of the hopper.

   Ⓐ 24 m³
   Ⓑ 54 m³
   Ⓒ 84 m³
   Ⓓ 124 m³

4. A cone with radius 2r and height 2h as shown in the diagram below contains liquid at a level equal to half the height of the cone. What fraction of the cone's volume is occupied by the liquid?

   Ⓐ 1/8
   Ⓑ 1/4
   Ⓒ 3/8
   Ⓓ 1/2

5. A cone has radius r and height h which is the same as a cylindrical can. The cone is filled with water then poured into the can. Find the ratio of the depth of the water to the height of the can.

   Ⓐ 1/9
   Ⓑ 1/6
   Ⓒ 1/3
   Ⓓ 1/2

6. Place the letter of the formula for calculating volume on the right in the blank that corresponds to the geometric figure that the formula applies to.

	$V = 1/3\ B\ h$	$V = 4/3\ \pi r^3$	$V = \pi r^2 h$	$V = 1/3\ \pi r^2 h$
Cylinder				
Cone				
Pyramid				
Sphere				

7. Andre wants to fill a cylindrical tank with water. If the tank has a diameter of 2 meters and is 3 meters high, how much water will Andre need? If necessary, use $\pi = 3.14$

   Ⓐ 8.14 m³
   Ⓑ 9.14 m³
   Ⓒ 9.42 m³
   Ⓓ 10.25 m³

8. Find the volume of a cone with a diameter of 4 feet and a height of 2 feet. If necessary use $\pi = 3.14$

   Ⓐ 8.373 m³
   Ⓑ 8.373 m²
   Ⓒ 23.03 m³
   Ⓓ 25.12 m³

9. Joe crafts a snowball that is 5 inches across at the diameter. Assume the snowball is a perfect sphere. Which value best represents the volume of the snowball? Use $\pi = 3.14$

   Ⓐ 47 in³
   Ⓑ 65 in³
   Ⓒ 52 in³
   Ⓓ 57 in³

10. Complete the following table with the correct formula. Simplify and leave answer in terms of π.

    Ⓐ V=166.67π mm³
    Ⓑ V=98π cm³
    Ⓒ V=16.67 ft³
    Ⓓ V=576 π cm³

11. A cube is sliced with a plane parallel to a face and passes through the center of the cube. What is the shape of the cross section that is created?

    Ⓐ Triangle
    Ⓑ Circle
    Ⓒ Square
    Ⓓ Ellipse

12. Given a cylinder, identify the shape of a cross section parallel to its base.

    Ⓐ Rectangle
    Ⓑ Circle
    Ⓒ Triangle
    Ⓓ Ellipse

13. Given a cylinder of diameter 7 cm and height 12 cm, find the area of the figure formed by passing a plane through the center of the cylinder perpendicular to the base?

    Ⓐ 14 cm²
    Ⓑ 28 cm²
    Ⓒ 42 cm²
    Ⓓ 84 cm²

14. An equilateral triangle with perimeter 30 cm is rotated about its altitude. Find the volume of the object generated. Express your answer in terms of π.

    Ⓐ $\frac{25}{3}253\pi$ cm³

    Ⓑ $\frac{25\sqrt{3}}{3}\pi$ cm³

    Ⓒ $\frac{125\sqrt{3}}{3}\pi$ cm³

    Ⓓ 125πcm³

15. **A circle with area 9πcm² is rotated about its diameter. Find the volume of the object generated. Express your answer in terms of π.**

Ⓐ 4π cm³
Ⓑ 12π cm³
Ⓒ 36π cm³
Ⓓ 108π cm³

16. **The cylinder shown below is sliced. Which of the following shapes could be a result?**

Ⓐ a triangle
Ⓑ a circle
Ⓒ a square
Ⓓ both A and B

17. **Which shape could result in an equilateral triangle if a cross section were taken?**

Ⓐ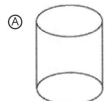

Ⓑ

Ⓒ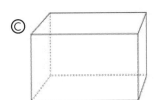

Ⓓ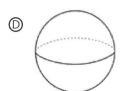

18. Given a sphere what shape can result from a cross section?

Ⓐ circle
Ⓑ oval
Ⓒ Both A & B
Ⓓ None of the Above

19. The rotation of a triangle when viewed from the top, would result what three dimensional shape?

Ⓐ sphere
Ⓑ circle
Ⓒ cone
Ⓓ cylinder

20. Looking at this shape from above would result in which shape?

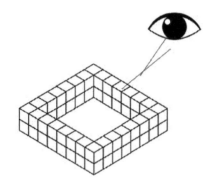

Ⓐ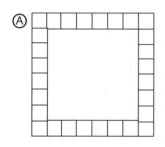

Ⓑ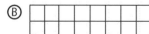

Ⓒ

Ⓓ

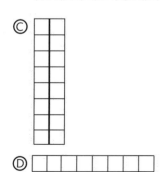

Chapter 6 - Modeling with Geometry

1. A farmer wishes to enclose a square plot of land with a fence so that he can grow a garden. Find the amount of fencing required if the length of a side is 15 ft.

   Ⓐ 45 ft
   Ⓑ 30 ft
   Ⓒ 225 ft
   Ⓓ 60 ft

2. The sail on a boat is in the shape of a right triangle. If the legs are 29.5 feet and 10.5 feet, what is the area of the sail rounded to the nearest whole number?

   Ⓐ 309 ft²
   Ⓑ 155 ft²
   Ⓒ 40 ft²
   Ⓓ 154 ft²

3. The sail on a boat is in the shape of a right triangle. If the legs are 5 feet and 10 feet, what is the perimeter of the triangle rounded to the nearest tenth?

   Ⓐ 140.3 ft
   Ⓑ 20.6 ft
   Ⓒ 26.2 ft
   Ⓓ 11.8 ft

4. The circular face of a watch has a diameter of 5 cm. What is the area of the face of the watch rounded to the nearest whole number?

   Ⓐ 79 cm
   Ⓑ 16 cm
   Ⓒ 20 cm
   Ⓓ 31 cm

5. A globe that models the shape of the earth has a diameter of 80 mm. What is the volume of the globe rounded to the nearest mm?

   Ⓐ 268,082 mm³
   Ⓑ 2,144,661 mm³
   Ⓒ 20,106 mm³
   Ⓓ 5,027 mm³

6. What is the area of a square with a perimeter of 4 feet?

    Ⓐ 1 ft
    Ⓑ 1 ft²
    Ⓒ 2 ft²
    Ⓓ 4 ft²

7. Four identical spheres are stacked in a cylinder. The edge of each sphere touches the side of the cylinder as shown. If the radius of the sphere is 4 cm, find the volume of the cylinder.

    Ⓐ 256πcm³
    Ⓑ 312πcm³
    Ⓒ 502πcm³
    Ⓓ 512πcm³

8. What is the density of a brick that occupies 310 cm³ with a mass of 853 g?

    Ⓐ 0.36 cm³/g
    Ⓑ 2.75 g/cm³
    Ⓒ 2.64 g/cm³
    Ⓓ 0.36 g/cm³

9. Diamond has a density of 3.26 g/cm³. What is the mass of a diamond that has a volume of .275 cm³?

    Ⓐ 0.897 g
    Ⓑ 11.855 g
    Ⓒ 0.084 g
    Ⓓ 10.957 g

10. Liquid mercury has a density of 13.6 g/mL. If a sample of liquid mercury has a mass of 85.4g, what is the volume of the mercury?

   Ⓐ 6.28 mL
   Ⓑ 0.16 mL
   Ⓒ 1161.44 mL
   Ⓓ 8.75 mL

11. If an unknown substance has a mass of 96.2 g and occupies $32.3cm^3$, what is the density of the substance?

   Ⓐ $2.98g/cm^3$
   Ⓑ $0.34g/cm^3$
   Ⓒ $3107.26g/cm^3$
   Ⓓ $4.76g/cm^3$

12. What volume would be occupied by 48.4 g of an unknown substance that has a density of $6.3g/cm^3$?

   Ⓐ $304.92 cm^3$
   Ⓑ $13.02 cm^3$
   Ⓒ $7.68 cm^3$
   Ⓓ $4.72 cm^3$

13. A 10 gallon round barrel is completely filled with water. If the density of water is about 8.3 lb/gal, how much does the water in the barrel weigh?

   Ⓐ 0.83 lbs
   Ⓑ 8.3 lbs
   Ⓒ 83 lbs
   Ⓓ 830 lbs

14. A perfectly spherical water balloon is filled with a liquid. The diameter of the balloon is 8 cm and it weighs 52 grams. What is the density of the liquid in the balloon?

   Ⓐ $0.32 g/cm^3$
   Ⓑ $0.20 g/cm^3$
   Ⓒ $0.02 g/cm^3$
   Ⓓ $20 g/cm^3$

15. A triangle has dimensions such that its longest side is 2 cm longer than twice its shortest side, and its remaining side is 4 cm longer than the shortest side. The perimeter of the triangle is 38 cm. Find the length of the shortest side.

Ⓐ 4cm
Ⓑ 8cm
Ⓒ 12cm
Ⓓ 16cm

16. A rectangular prism with height h has a square base with lengths x. If its dimensions were doubled, its volume would increase by 315cm³. Find the volume of the prism.

Ⓐ 15cm³
Ⓑ 30cm³
Ⓒ 45cm³
Ⓓ 60cm³

17. A cube has lengths x on each side. If its dimensions were doubled, its surface area would increase by 162cm². Find x.

Ⓐ 2 cm
Ⓑ 3 cm
Ⓒ 4 cm
Ⓓ 6 cm

18. A rectangle has a length equal to twice its width. If its length and width are each made 2 cm longer, its area will increase by 52cm². Find the original width of the rectangle.

Ⓐ 2 cm
Ⓑ 4 cm
Ⓒ 8 cm
Ⓓ 16 cm

19. A 20 cm x 16 cm piece of cardboard is used to make a box in the shape of a rectangular prism. A 4 cm square is cut out of each corner, and the sides are folded up to form the box. Find the volume of the resulting box.

Ⓐ 48cm³
Ⓑ 96cm³
Ⓒ 192cm³
Ⓓ 384cm³

20. An arc of radius 4 cm is drawn inside a square with side lengths of 4 cm as shown in the diagram. What is the area of the shaded region?

4 cm

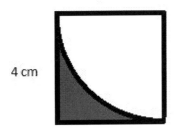

4 cm

Ⓐ 1.72 cm²
Ⓑ 3.43 cm²
Ⓒ 6.29 cm²
Ⓓ 12.57 cm²

Chapter 7 - Conditional Probability and the Rules of Probability

1. Market analysts from an automobile manufacturing company randomly sampled 500 new car buyers for a survey on their new car preferences. The data from the survey is in the table below.

	V8	V6	Total
Candy Apple Red	105	73	178
Black Pearl	87	76	163
Royal Blue	108	51	159
Total	300	200	500

Based on the survey, what is the probability that a randomly selected new car buyer would want a Candy Apple Red car with a V8?

Ⓐ 21.6 %
Ⓑ 15.3 %
Ⓒ 21 %
Ⓓ 17.4 %

2. Set A = {1, 2, 3, 4, 5}. Set B = { 1, 2, 3}. Set C = {3, 4, 5}. What is the union and intersection of Sets A and B?

Ⓐ A U B = {1, 2, 3, 4, 5}
    A ∩ B = {3}

Ⓑ A U B = {1, 2, 3, 4, 5}
    A ∩ B = {1, 2, 3}

Ⓒ A U B = {1, 2, 3}
    A ∩ B = {1, 2, 3, 4, 5}

Ⓓ A U B = {1, 2, 3, 4, 5}
    A ∩ B = {4, 5, 6}

3. The sample space of tossing a coin and rolling a dice is the set {T1,H1,T2,H2,T3,H3T4, H4,T5,H5,T6,H6} where H means heads and T means tails. Which set is the set of {: H Even Number}?

Ⓐ {H2, H4, H6}
Ⓑ {T2,T4,T6}
Ⓒ {T1,T3,T5}
Ⓓ {T1,T2,T3,T4,T5,T6}

4. A standard deck of playing cards has 52 cards, with 13 hearts, 13 clubs, 13 spades, and 13 diamonds. Suppose you randomly pick a card and it is a diamond, but you do not replace the card back into the deck. What is the probability of randomly picking another diamond, and are these two events independent or dependent?

Ⓐ $\frac{12}{51}$ - independent

Ⓑ $\frac{12}{51}$ - dependent

Ⓒ $\frac{1}{4}$ - dependent

Ⓓ $\frac{1}{4}$ - independent

5. A standard deck of playing cards has 52 cards, with 13 hearts, 13 clubs, 13 spades, and 13 diamonds. Suppose you randomly pick a card and it is a spade, then you replace the card back into the deck. What is the probability of randomly picking another spade, and are these two events independent or dependent?

Ⓐ $\frac{12}{51}$ - independent

Ⓑ $\frac{1}{4}$ - dependent

Ⓒ $\frac{12}{51}$ - dependent

Ⓓ $\frac{1}{4}$ - independent

6. Suppose you have a bag of colored marbles that contains 25 purple marbles and 25 pink marbles. You reach into the bag, without looking, and draw out a purple marble. Then, you reach into the bag again and draw out another purple marble without replacing the first purple marble. Are these two events independent of each other or dependent of each other?

Ⓐ independent
Ⓑ dependent
Ⓒ neither
Ⓓ cannot be determined

7. Juan has 25 coins in a bag, including 10 dimes and 15 quarters. He reaches into the bag and pulls out a coin. Then he reaches into the bag again and pulls out another coin. What is the probability that Juan pulls out a quarter as the second coin, given that he pulls out a quarter as the first coin as well?

Ⓐ $\frac{5}{12}$

Ⓑ $\frac{3}{5}$

Ⓒ $\frac{7}{12}$

Ⓓ $\frac{2}{5}$

8. A survey of all of the members of an outdoor youth camp asked the camp attendees to identify which outdoor activity they most preferred to participate in next week. The result of the survey is in the table below. What is the probability that a randomly selected attendee is interested in hiking given that the student is a girl?

	Hiking	Kayaking	Total
Boys	65	72	137
Girls	50	63	113
Total	115	135	250

Ⓐ $\frac{1}{5}$

Ⓑ $\frac{10}{23}$

Ⓒ $\frac{23}{50}$

Ⓓ $\frac{50}{113}$

9. Juan has 30 coins in a bag, including 12 dimes and 18 quarters. He reaches into the bag and pulls out a coin. Then he reaches into the bag again and pulls out another coin. What is the probability that Juan pulls out a quarter as the second coin, given that he pulls out a quarter as the first coin as well?

Ⓐ $\frac{9}{15}$

Ⓑ $\frac{10}{29}$

Ⓒ $\frac{17}{30}$

Ⓓ $\frac{17}{29}$

10. A survey of students in a college class was conducted among men and women to record their preference of ice cream or yogurt. The partial result of the survey is in the table.

	Ice Cream	Yogurt	Total
Men	X	73	94
Women	59	Y	94
Total	80	108	Z

Based on the numbers in the table, what are the values of X, Y, and Z?

Ⓐ X = 31, Y=25, Z=188
Ⓑ X = 21, Y=35, Z=188
Ⓒ X = 21, Y=45, Z=198
Ⓓ X = 31, Y=25, Z=178

11. The human resources department of a major company conducted a survey of 250 employees to determine their preference of working at home or working in the office. The result of the survey is partially shown in the table.

	Home	Office	Total
Men	92	?	151
Women	?	81	99
Total	110	140	250

Based on the information in the table, how many men preferred to work in the office and how many women preferred to work at home?

Ⓐ 18, 59
Ⓑ 21, 57
Ⓒ 59, 18
Ⓓ 58, 21

12. A survey of 5th and 6th graders was conducted to see whether they did their homework using a pen or a pencil. The result of the survey is partially shown in the table.

	Pen	Pencil	Total
5th	6	29	
6th	4	21	
Total	D	E	F

Based on the numbers in the table, what are the values of D, E and F?

Ⓐ D=10, E=50, F=60
Ⓑ D=50, E=10, F=60
Ⓒ D=60, E=50, F=10
Ⓓ D=10, E=60, F=50

13. A point is chosen at random on $\overline{AE}$. What is the probability that the point lies on $\overline{BC}$?

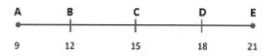

  Ⓐ $\dfrac{1}{3}$

  Ⓑ $\dfrac{1}{4}$

  Ⓒ $\dfrac{1}{5}$

  Ⓓ $\dfrac{1}{2}$

14. Which would not be a good label to represent the following situation in a two-way frequency table?
    Is there a relationship between people who have blonde hair and people who like cake?

  Ⓐ People who have brown hair
  Ⓑ People who have blonde hair
  Ⓒ People who like cake
  Ⓓ People who don't have blonde hair

15. Given the following two-way frequency table groupings, what would you need to calculate to find the probability that a person is blonde and prefers to go to the movies?

  Group 1: Blonde hair (B), Red hair (R)
  Group 2: Prefers movies P(M), Prefers Bowling (W)

  Ⓐ P(B)-P(M)
  Ⓑ P(M|B)
  Ⓒ P(B|M)
  Ⓓ P(B)+P(M)

16. A report shows that in a high school with 400 students, there are 40% girls. The report says that 20% of the students in the school wear glasses. It is also known that 10% of the boys wear glasses. How many boys wear glasses?

  Ⓐ 24
  Ⓑ 240
  Ⓒ 16
  Ⓓ 160

17. A report shows that in a high school with 400 students, there are 40% girls. The report says that 20% of the students in the school wear glasses. It is also known that 10% of the boys wear glasses. How many boys are in this school?

Ⓐ 160
Ⓑ 240
Ⓒ 80
Ⓓ 200

18. A study found that in a small town, 40% of all households have a pet and 35% have children living at home. The report also found that 60% of all households with children living at home have a pet. If a household in the town is selected at random, what is the probability that household has children living at home and has a pet?

Ⓐ 21%
Ⓑ 26%
Ⓒ 24%
Ⓓ 40%

19. Suppose the probability that event C occurs is 0.4, the probability that event D occurs is 0.6, and the probability that both events C and D occur is 0.2. What is the probability that event C or event D occurs?

Ⓐ 0.3
Ⓑ 0.2
Ⓒ 0.8
Ⓓ 1.2

20. Suppose the probability that event G occurs is 0.35, the probability that event H occurs is 0.45, and the probability that both events G and H occur is 0.25. What is the probability that either event G occurs or event H occurs?

Ⓐ 0.90
Ⓑ 1.05
Ⓒ 0.35
Ⓓ 0.55

Chapter 8 - Using Probability to Make Decisions

1. Items that are used in a fair decision making process should be checked for what?

   Ⓐ Different shapes
   Ⓑ Different sizes
   Ⓒ Different weights
   Ⓓ All of these

2. Which decision making tool would be considered fair?

   Ⓐ Tossing a fair die
   Ⓑ Using a random number generator
   Ⓒ Both A and B
   Ⓓ None of these

3. You are collecting data by flipping a coin and recording the results. You flip the coin 4 times and get tails all four times. What could be right about the situation?

   Ⓐ This is an unfair coin
   Ⓑ This is a fair coin
   Ⓒ The result is due to chance
   Ⓓ All of the above

4. You may have seen on television when the lottery numbers are drawn they use a machine that sucks the balls up one by one until they have all the numbers necessary. If the machine they use keeps pulling the same ball over and over again from week to week, what may be happening?

   Ⓐ Nothing it's just due to chance
   Ⓑ The ball may be lighter than the others
   Ⓒ The ball may be a slightly different shape
   Ⓓ All of these

5. Your mom and dad always argue over the last slice of pie at Thanksgiving. What is the most fair and unbiased way to settle this disagreement?

   Ⓐ Let your mom flip a coin
   Ⓑ Let someone who doesn't have any interest in your mom, dad, or the pie flip a coin
   Ⓒ Let your paternal grandmother flip a coin
   Ⓓ Let someone who doesn't have any interest in your mom, dad, or the pie choose who gets it

6. Why is tossing a normal die a fair way to make a decision?

     Ⓐ It has no bias as to how it lands
     Ⓑ It has 6 sides
     Ⓒ All of the above
     Ⓓ None of the above

7. Is playing a game of Texas Hold'em a fair way to make a decision?
   Texas Hold'em is a variation of the card game of poker.

     Ⓐ Yes, each player has a chance to make decisions
     Ⓑ Yes, each player gets a random set of cards to play with
     Ⓒ No, psychology and manipulation play too much of a role in this type of card game

8. You are going out to eat with 2 friends. You are all hungry for a completely different restaurant. What is the most fair way to pick which restaurant you will eat at?

     Ⓐ Let the person who is driving decide
     Ⓑ Draw lots
     Ⓒ Flip a coin
     Ⓓ Roll a die

9. In what situation would a statistically sound fair outcome be unfair in reality?

     Ⓐ When the outcome has life or death consequences
     Ⓑ When the outcome makes someone mad
     Ⓒ When someone thinks the outcome is unfair
     Ⓓ All of these

10. A produce stand manager charged Luca $8 for 6 cucumbers. The sign on the bin of cucumbers advertises a price of $10 per dozen. Which statement is true about the fairness of the price the manager charged Luca?

     Ⓐ The price was fair. To get the best deal, Luca should buy a dozen cucumbers.
     Ⓑ The price is not fair. To be fair, the manager should have charged Luca about $5.
     Ⓒ The price was fair. Each cucumber costs more if you don't buy a whole dozen.
     Ⓓ The price was not fair. The manager should have charged Luca about $7.

11. A car manufacturer knows that for every 100 airbags they install in their cars 1 will malfunction opening the manufacturer up to millions of dollars in costly litigation. Would it be a good strategy to raise the price of each car by $100 to cover the cost of litigation?

Ⓐ Yes, this litigation is a major cost to the manufacturer
Ⓑ Yes, the manufacturer should not have to pay for faulty airbags
Ⓒ No, a car is an expensive item and the manufacturer has many other costs to consider
Ⓓ No, the customer should not have to pay extra because of faulty airbags.

12. The odds of getting struck by lightning in the United States in any one year is 1 in 700,000. Would it be fair to say that if there were 700,000 people swimming in pools during a thunderstorm that only one of them would get struck?

Ⓐ Yes
Ⓑ No
Ⓒ Maybe
Ⓓ Not enough information

13. A research company is testing four different appetite suppressants. The people chosen are randomly selected for the study but the types of appetite suppressants they are given are not randomly assigned. Despite the people for the study being randomly selected, why is not assigning the types of appetite suppressants randomly a problem?

Ⓐ Selection bias based on the researchers' preference could enter the study
Ⓑ The lack of random assignment won't be a problem
Ⓒ Giving appetite suppressants to random people could be harmful to their health
Ⓓ None of these

14. Companies hire market researchers to figure out whether or not a new product will be popular. Which of the following would be best for the market research company to do when gathering data to back up their findings?

Ⓐ Sample random people
Ⓑ Sample people that are most likely to use the new product
Ⓒ Sample people who are least likely to use the new product
Ⓓ All of these

15. If the expected value of betting on a baseball game is $60, but it costs $75 to make the bet, which of the following is true?

Ⓐ You shouldn't play since you will lost money in the long run
Ⓑ You should play because it's less about the money and more about the game
Ⓒ You should play because there's always a chance you will win
Ⓓ All of the above

16. How could a company who is considering marketing a new product best come up with important sales probabilities?

    Ⓐ Asking a psychic
    Ⓑ Research and focus groups
    Ⓒ Advertising the new product
    Ⓓ None of these

17. Why is making decisions based on larger samples considered better than making decisions based on small samples?

    Ⓐ There is no difference in the two
    Ⓑ Small samples are more accurate
    Ⓒ Large samples are more accurate
    Ⓓ None of these

18. A company is considering building a plant in two different counties. They hire a geologist to advise them as to which soil would be best for growing cotton. The geologist is not very familiar with the land in either county so how could he best gather data to help him in deciding which county to recommend?

    Ⓐ Toss a coin
    Ⓑ Talk to the officials in each county
    Ⓒ Take soil samples and run studies on each county
    Ⓓ None of these

19. A game show host is going to draw a random number from 1 to 25. Contestants can place one of two bets before the drawing. Bet A costs $10 to place. If the drawing produces a number that is odd, the bet returns a prize of $18. Otherwise, it returns nothing. Bet B costs $15 to place. If the drawing produces a number that is a multiple of 4, the bet returns a prize of $100. Otherwise, it returns nothing. Which bet is the better deal?

    Ⓐ Bet A
    Ⓑ Bet B
    Ⓒ The bets have the same net value
    Ⓓ Cannot be determined

20. A charity booth at a town carnival is holding two different raffles. Raffle A sold 1,000 tickets. Each ticket costs $3. The payout for the winning ticket is $1000. The other tickets receive nothing. Raffle B sold 250 tickets. Each ticket costs $5. One ticket will win $300, one ticket will win $150, and one ticket will win $75. No one can win more than one prize. All other tickets receive nothing. Which raffle is a better deal?

Ⓐ Raffle A
Ⓑ Raffle B
Ⓒ Both raffles have the same net value
Ⓓ Cannot be determined

Answer Key &
Detailed Explanations

Chapter 1 - Congruence

Question No.	Answer	Detailed Explanation
1	C	A point is the building block in geometry. Thus, all figures consist of points. A point is an exact position or location on a plane surface. It is important to understand that a point is not a thing, but a place. We indicate the position of a point by placing a dot with a pencil. This dot may represent a point, but a point has no size; no width, no length, and no height. No matter how far you zoomed in on a point, it would still have no width, no length, and no height.
2	B	A line is defined as a set of points on a plane that extend in two directions without ending. Thus, a line is one-dimensional. It has a length, but zero width. If you draw a line with a pencil, and examine it with a microscope, it would show that the pencil mark has a measurable width. The pencil line is just a way to illustrate the idea on paper. In geometry however, a line has no width.
3	B	The coordinates of point A are (-6,2) . If we translate the point 5 units downward, we must subtract from the y-value in the point. Therefore, the coordinates of point A' are (-6, 2-5) = (-6, -3).
4	D	The coordinates of point A are (4, 3). If we reflect a point across the y-axis, the x-value in the point changes sign. The x-coordinate in point A is 4. The reflection changes it to -4. Therefore, the coordinates of point A' are (-4, 3).
5	C	The image below shows an example of ABCD in quadrant I reflected across the y-axis, forming A'B'C'D' . Then reflected across the x-axis forming A"B"C"D". Then, the figure shows the lines of reflection across the origin. Notice that A"B"C"D" reflects back onto ABCD in quadrant I. 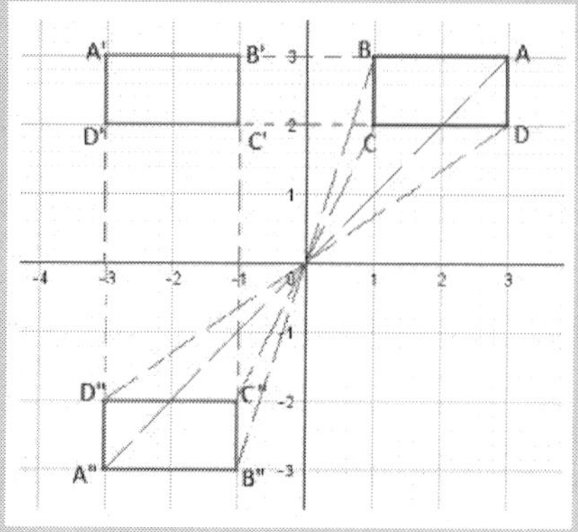

Question No.	Answer	Detailed Explanation
6	B	Based on the two graphs, the triangle is translated 9 units to the right and 11 units down. This is the translation rule $(x, y) \rightarrow (x+9, y-11)$.
7	B	The order of the labeled vertices does not change, as all of the choices show. However, the corresponding position of each vertex or corner in the figure must not change. Only one figure keeps the labeled vertices in the correct corresponding position.
8	D	The question states that quadrilateral ABCD is rotated 30^0 counter clockwise about vertex C. The given figure also shows quadrilateral ABCD with slanted sides. Only one choice shows both the original quadrilateral ABCD with slanted sides and the center of rotation at vertex C.
9	D	The reflection over the x-axis would move the point from $(1, 2)$ to $(1, -2)$. Next, the translation would move the point to $(3, -1)$.
10	B	By looking at polygon, ABCD, we see that the coordinates are as below: A $(5,1)$, B$(8,0)$, C$(7, -2)$ and D $(5, -1)$ When we translate 2 units to left and 1 unit down, we get the points $(3,0)$, $(6,-1)$, $(5, -2)$ and $(3, -2)$ When we reflect it over $x = 2$, we get the points $(1,0)$, $(-2,-1)$, $(-1,-3)$ and $(1, -2)$ which is the coordinates of A'B'C'D'. Hence, answer choice B is correct.
11	B	Rotations and reflections preserve the length and measure of angles and therefore the image will be congruent to the original image.
12	C	If a transformation is a rigid motion, the shape and size of the original object does not change. A translation is a sliding movement, a rotation is a turning movement, and a reflection is an image that looks opposite. These are all rigid motions. A dilation changes the size of the original object, making it larger or smaller, but the same shape.
13	D	By having the ladder slide over, it is a translation. Since all of the angles and lengths are preserved, they are congruent
14	B	Dilations do not preserve the lengths and therefore the triangles are not congruent.
15	C	Only answer choice C matches with congruency postulate. In this case, it is the SAS rule gets applied. The sides and the angles must be incorrect order such as the corresponding side and included angle. Hence, answer choice C is correct.

Question No.	Answer	Detailed Explanation
16	D	From the figure we can see that AC ≅ CD and ∠DCB ≅ ∠ABC. We also know that a shared side CB is congruent with itself. However, the relationship of these parts are not the same in both triangles. One is SSA and the other one is SAS. Therefore, the two triangles are not necessarily congruent by any triangle congruence method, thus validating that ΔABC → ΔDCB does not represent some type of rigid motion.
17	C	Not all angles on the same side of a transversal are supplementary. If the angles were interior same side angles that were supplementary than it would prove that the lines are parallel.
18	C	The question does not provide any information about the length of the sides of the two triangles, but the question states that m∠4= m∠6; m∠1=m∠3; m∠4=m∠5; ∠DEB ≅ ∠DCB. Since m∠4= m∠6, ∠4 ≅ ∠6, AD ≅ BD because of isosceles triangle properties. This information indicates that at least two corresponding angles in the two triangles are congruent and the ratio of the sides is 1.1. Thus, by the ASA triangle congruence theorem, we can state that the triangles are congruent: ΔBDE ≅ ΔBAD.
19	D	The questions states that ABCD is a parallelogram. A property of parallelograms is that the diagonals bisect each other. If a diagonal is bisected, it is divided into two equal parts. Therefore, we can use this property to write and solve an equation to find x: x + 40 = 2x + 18. So, X = 22. Now we can find the length of each segment of DB, which are equal to each other. x + 40 = 22 + 40 = 62; 2(22) + 18 = 62. Add the two parts: 62 + 62 = 124 the length of BD is 124.
20	C	A square has four sides that all have congruent lengths.

Chapter 2 - Similarity, Right Triangles, and Trigonometry

Question No.	Answer	Detailed Explanation
1	B	When a dilation is performed about the origin, the coordinates of the image point are the product of the scale factor and the coordinates of the original point. $2 \times 3 = 6$. $2 \times 4 = 8$.
2	C	When a dilation is performed about the origin, the coordinates of the image point are the product of the scale factor and the coordinates of the original point. $3 \times -3 = -9$. $3 \times 2 = 6$.
3	A	When a dilation is performed about the origin, the coordinates of the image point are the product of the scale factor and the coordinates of the original point. $\frac{1}{2} \times 4 = 2$. $\frac{1}{2} \times -3 = -3/2$.
4	C	Since the triangles are similar, the sides of the triangle are in proportion to each other. $\frac{6.29 \text{ m}}{x} = \frac{6 \text{ m}}{10 \text{ m}}$; solving the equation for x yields x = 10.5 m.
5	B	Since the triangles are similar, the sides of the triangle are in proportion to each other. $\frac{3.19 \text{ m}}{y} = \frac{6 \text{ m}}{10 \text{ m}}$; solving the equation for y yields y = 5.32 m.
6	D	Since the triangles are similar, the sides of the triangle are in proportion to each other. $\frac{4 \text{ m}}{y} = \frac{8 \text{ m}}{14 \text{ m}}$; solving the equation for x yields x = 7.00 m.
7	A	The AA Postulate proves that two triangles are similar. Since we were given that $\angle K \cong \angle B$ and we can see that $\overline{JB}$ and $\overline{KA}$ intersect and form vertical angles at point C, those angles are congruent.
8	C	We have been given, $\overline{WX}$ and $\overline{YZ}$ and $\overline{YW}$ and $\overline{ZX}$ are transversals. Thus makes, $\angle X = \angle Z$ and $\angle W = \angle Y$ because parallel lines cut by a transversal, then the alternate interior angles formed are congruent. Also, we have $\angle XQW = \angle YQZ$. Therefore, by AAA postulate, we have $\triangle XQW$ is congruent to $\triangle YQZ$.
9	B	Since $\triangle QXW \sim \triangle QZY$ by the AA Postulate, the ratio of the corresponding sides are equal. Therefore, $\frac{WQ}{YQ} = \frac{XQ}{ZQ}$. So, $\frac{4}{3} = \frac{a}{5}$. Solving the proportion yields $a = \frac{20}{3}$.

Question No.	Answer	Detailed Explanation
10	A	The Pythagorean Theorem, $c^2 = a^2 + b^2$ where c is the hypotenuse, is used to find missing sides in a right triangle. Substitute 3 for a and 4 for b. Solve for c to find the hypotenuse. $c^2 = a^2 + b^2$ Substituting, we get, $c^2 = 3^2 + 4^2$ $c^2 = 9 + 16 = 25$ Hence, c= AC = 5
11	A	Since $\overline{RS}$ is parallel to $\overline{BC}$, $\angle ARS \cong \angle ABC$ because parallel lines cut by a transversal form corresponding angles that are congruent. Since $\angle A \cong \angle A$, $\triangle ABC \sim \triangle ARS$ by the AA Postulate. When triangles are similar, the ratio of their sides are proportional. Therefore, $\frac{AR}{AB} = \frac{AS}{AC}$. Substituting the values, we get, $\frac{5}{13} = \frac{x}{6+x}$ Cross multiplying, $5(6+x) = 13x$ $30 + 5x = 13x$ $30 = (13-5)x$ $30 = 8x$ Therefore, x = 30/8 = 3.75
12	C	Since $\overline{YB}$ is parallel to $\overline{XA}$, $\angle ZYB \cong \angle ZXA$ because parallel lines cut by a transversal form corresponding angles that are congruent. Since $\angle Z \cong \angle Z$, $\triangle ZXA \sim \triangle ZYB$ by the AA Postulate. When triangles are similar, the ratio of their sides are proportional. Therefore, $\frac{ZY}{ZX} = \frac{ZB}{ZA}$. Substituting we get, $\frac{6}{13} = \frac{x}{x+14}$ Cross Multiplying we get, $6(x+14) = 13x$ $6x + 84 = 13x$ $84 = (13-6)x$ $84 = 7x$ Therefore, x = 84/7 = 12
13	A	When triangles are congruent, corresponding parts are also congruent. Since $\angle A$ corresponds to $\angle E$, A=30°. Then all angles in a triangle must add up to 180°, $\angle C$=26°.
14	C	When a congruence statement for triangles is written, the corresponding vertices of the triangle should always be listed in the same order. Therefore GH = RS, HI = ST, and GI = RT.
15	B	The two triangles are similar using the AA similarity theorem because two corresponding angles in one triangle are congruent to two corresponding angles in the other triangle. When writing a triangle similarity statement, pay particular attention to which angles correspond to each other. The angles with the same measure correspond. Therefore, $\angle X$ corresponds to $\angle U$, $\angle Y$ corresponds to $\angle V$, and then, by default, $\angle W$ corresponds to $\angle T$. Then, write the similarity statement lining up the corresponding angles in the same order in each triangle: $\triangle WXY \sim \triangle TUV$

Question No.	Answer	Detailed Explanation
16	B	The two triangles are similar using the AA similarity theorem because two corresponding angles in one triangle are congruent to two corresponding angles in the other triangle. When writing a triangle similarity statement, pay particular attention to which angles correspond to each other. The angles with the same measure correspond. Therefore, $\angle B$ corresponds to $\angle Z$, $\angle C$ corresponds to $\angle Y$, and then, by default, $\angle A$ corresponds to $\angle X$. The figure shows that the $m\angle B = m\angle Z = 50°$ and $m\angle C = m\angle Y = 103°$ Then, write the similarity statement lining up the corresponding angles in the same order in each triangle: $\triangle ABC \sim \triangle XZY$
17	C	In a right triangle, the sine of one of the acute angles is the same as the cosine of the other acute angle. The trigonometric ratios in the triangle are $\cos \theta = \dfrac{\text{Adjacent}}{\text{Hypotenuse}}$ and $\sin \theta = \dfrac{\text{Opposite}}{\text{Hypotenuse}}$. Therefore, $\cos P = \dfrac{12}{20} = \dfrac{3}{5}$, $\sin R = \dfrac{12}{20} = \dfrac{3}{5}$, $\sin P = \dfrac{16}{20} = \dfrac{4}{5}$, and $\cos R = \dfrac{16}{20} = \dfrac{4}{5}$.
18	C	In a right triangle, the sine of one of the acute angles is the same as the cosine of the other acute angle. The trigonometric ratios in the triangle are $\cos \theta = \dfrac{\text{Adjacent}}{\text{Hypotenuse}}$ and $\sin \theta = \dfrac{\text{Opposite}}{\text{Hypotenuse}}$. Therefore, $\cos K = \dfrac{5}{13}$, $\sin L = \dfrac{5}{13}$, $\sin K = \dfrac{12}{13}$, and $\cos L = \dfrac{12}{13}$.
19	B	The question states that a building casts a shadow that is 11 feet long and the distance from the top of the building to the end of the shadow is 61 feet. Since the building forms a right angle with the ground, this situation can be represented by a right triangle. In the right triangle, the sides are the height of the building and the length of the shadow. The hypotenuse is the distance from the top of the building to the end of the shadow. Use the Pythagorean Theorem to find the height of the building. The theorem uses the formula $a^2 + b = c^2$ where a and b are the sides of the triangle and c is the hypotenuse. Substituting the values given in the question, the formula changes to $a^2 + 11^2 = 61^2$. The variable a is the height of the building. Solving or a: $a^2 + 121 = 3721$; $a^2 = 3600$; $a = 60$. The building is 60 feet tall.
20	A	Use the Pythagorean Theorem to find the length of the hypotenuse. The theorem uses the formula $a^2 + b = c^2$ where a and b are the sides of the triangle and c is the hypotenuse. Substituting the values given in the question, the formula changes to $8^2 + 15^2 = c^2$. The variable c is the length of the hypotenuse. Solving or c: $64 + 225 = c^2$; $c^2 = 289$; $c = 17$. The length of the hypotenuse is 17.

Chapter 3 - Circles

Question No.	Answer	Detailed Explanation
1	B	Since the diameter of a circle is twice the radius, the ratio $\frac{d_1}{d_2}$ $= \frac{2r_1}{2r_2}$; therefore the ratio of the diameters will be equal to the ratio of the radii. $\frac{d_1}{d_2} = \frac{4 \text{ cm}}{2 \text{ cm}} = 2$.
2	C	Since the circumference of a circle is related to the radius by $C = 2\pi u p r$, the ratio of the circumferences of two circles of different radii will be $\frac{C_1}{C_2} = \frac{2\pi r_1}{2\pi r_2}$; therefore the ratio of the circumferences will reduce to the ratio of the radii. [$\frac{C_1}{C_2} = \frac{8 \text{ cm}}{2 \text{ cm}} = 4$]
3	B	Since the circumference of a circle is related to the diameter by $C = \pi d$, the ratio of the circumferences of two circles of different diameters will be $\frac{C_1}{C_2} = \frac{\pi r_1}{\pi r_2}$; therefore the ratio of the circumferences will reduce to the ratio of the diameters. [$\frac{C_1}{C_2} = \frac{20 \text{ cm}}{4 \text{ cm}} = 5$]
4	C	Since the area of a circle is related to the radius by $A = \pi r^2$, the ratio of the areas of two circles of different diameters will be $\frac{A_1}{A_2} = \frac{\pi r_1^2}{\pi r_2^2}$; therefore the ratio of the areas will reduce to the ratio of the square of the radii of the two circles. $\frac{A_1}{A_2} = (\frac{15 \text{ cm}}{3 \text{ cm}})^2 = 25$
5	B	The original circle F has its center at the point $(-6, 6)$ with a radius of 4 units. The translated/dilated circle F' has its center at the point $(-2, -8)$ with a radius of 2 units. This means the center was translated right 4 units and down 14 units. As a transformation, this translation is written as $(x, y) \rightarrow (x+4, y-14)$. Circle F was also dilated by a factor of ½ because the radius was reduced from 4 units to 2 units. As a transformation, this dilation is written as $(x, y) \rightarrow \frac{1}{2}(x, y)$. Putting the translation and dilation together, the rule is $(x, y) \rightarrow \frac{1}{2}(x+4, y-14)$.
6	B	Since points A and C form the same intercepted arc for the central angle, $\angle ABC$, and the inscribed angle, $\angle ADC$, the measure of the inscribed angle, $\angle ADC$, will be half the measure of the central angle, $\angle ABC$. Therefore $\angle ADC = 60°$.

Question No.	Answer	Detailed Explanation
7	A	Since points A and C form the same intercepted arc for the central angle, ∠ABC, and the inscribed angle, ∠ADC, the measure of the inscribed angle, ∠ADC, will be half the measure of the central angle, ∠ABC. Therefore m∠ADC=40°. Since line segment BD bisects ∠ADC(given), m∠BDA=m∠BDC=20°. BD=BC= the radius of the circle, therefore ΔBDC is an isosceles triangle with m∠BDC=∠BCD=20°.
8	B	A corollary to the Inscribed Angle Theorem states that the measures of opposite angles in a quadrilateral that is inscribed in a circle are supplementary angles. The sum of the measures of supplementary angles is 180°. Quadrilateral ABCD is inscribed in circle O, and ∠DAB is opposite ∠BCD, and m∠BCD=110°, as shown in the figure. Therefore, ∠DAB=70° because 110+70=180.
9	B	A geometric theorem states that the perpendicular bisector of a chord passes through the center of the circle. The figure shows that the line that contains segment OB passes through the center, at point O and intersects chord AC. Thus, the chord is bisected and since segment mBC=15, mAB=15. Therefore, x=15.
10	B	A geometric theorem states that the perpendicular bisector of a chord passes through the center of the circle. The figure shows that the line that contains segment OC passes through the center, at point O and intersects chord AB. Thus, OC⊥AB, and AC≅CB. Thus, mAC=4, and ΔAOC is a right triangle. Use the Pythagorean Theorem to find the length of OC or the value of x; $x^2+4^2=5^2$; x=3.
11	C	Since circle O is inscribed inside ΔABC, segments OA, OB, and OC bisect the vertex angles. Therefore m∠DAO = ½ m∠A=40°.
12	B	Since m∠BFO=90°, OF is perpendicular to FB. Circle O circumscribes ΔABC, therefore O must lie on the perpendicular bisector of AB. AF = ½ AB ; AF = ½ (12 cm) = 6 cm.
13	D	When a quadrilateral is circumscribed by a circle, opposite angles of the quadrilateral will be supplementary. m∠A+m∠C=180°; m∠C=180°−100°=80°.
14	A	A geometry theorem states that the tangent segments from a point outside the circle to two tangent points on the circle are congruent. Thus, VZ≅WZ, WX≅UX, and UY≅VY. Then, mVZ=mWZ=4, mWX=mUX=8, and mUY=mVY=9. Now, by the Segment Addition Postulate, mXY=8+9=17.

Question No.	Answer	Detailed Explanation
15	B	A geometry theorem states that the tangent segments from a point outside the circle to two tangent points on the circle are congruent. Thus, $\overline{AX} \cong \overline{AZ}$, $\overline{BX} \cong \overline{BY}$, and $\overline{CY} \cong \overline{CZ}$. Then, $m\overline{AX} = m\overline{AZ} = 8$, $m\overline{BX} = m\overline{BY} = 10$, and $m\overline{CY} = m\overline{CZ} = 4$. Now, by the Segment Addition Postulate, $m\overline{BC} = 10 + 4 = 14$.
16	B	Arc length $= r\theta$; therefore length $= (12\text{ft})(\frac{7}{4}\pi) = 21\pi\text{ft}$
17	C	Arc length $= r\theta$; therefore length $= (18\text{ft})(\frac{2}{3}\pi) = 12\pi\text{ft}$
18	B	$\text{Area} = \frac{\theta}{2\pi}\pi r^2 = \frac{\theta}{2}r^2$; therefore $\text{Area} = \frac{\pi/3}{2}(6 \text{ cm})^2 = 6\pi\text{cm}^2$
19	C	The area of a circle is calculated using the formula $A = \pi r^2$, where A is the area and r is the radius. The area of a sector of a circle is calculated using the formula $A = \frac{b}{360} \times \pi r^2$, where b is the degrees of the sector of the circle. The figure shows that the radius is 4 in and the sector has a measure of 95°. Thus, the approximate area is $A = \frac{95}{360} \times (3.14)(4)^2 = 13.258 \text{ in}^2$.
20	D	The circumference of a circle is the distance around the circle, and is calculated with the formula $C = 2\pi r$. An arc is a part of the circumference and the length of an arc in a circle is calculated using the formula $L = \theta r$, where L is the length of the arc, θ is the measure of the angle in radians, and r is the radius. The figure shows that the radius is 28 mm and the sector has a measure of 135°. Convert the angle to radians by multiplying by $\frac{\theta}{180°}$. Thus, the measure of the angle in radians is $180° \times \frac{\pi}{180°} = \pi$. Therefore, the length of the arc is $L = \pi \times 28 \text{ mm} = 28\pi \text{ mm}$.

Chapter 4 - Expressing Geometric Properties with Equations

Question No.	Answer	Detailed Explanation
1	A	Rules: Equation of a Circle: $(x-h)^2+(y-k)^2=r^2$; C(h,k); r=radius Using the formula for the equation of a circle above. Substitute the h and k values of the center into the equation and the radius. Don't forget to square the radius.
2	C	Rules: Equation of a Circle: $(x-h)^2+(y-k)^2=r^2$; C(h,k); r=radius Use the formula for the equation of a circle above. Therefore, h = -1, k = 7, and r =$\sqrt{23}$. The coordinates for the center of a circle are (h, k) so (-1, 7) is the center of this circle and the radius = $\sqrt{23}$.
3	D	Rules: Equation of a Circle: $(x-h)^2+(y-k)^2=r^2$; C(h,k); r=radius A circle in standard position is centered at (0, 0). Since this circle has its center at (2, -3) that means it has shifted right 2 units and down three units. The radius =$\sqrt{16}$=4.
4	C	Rules: Equation of a Circle: $(x-h)^2+(y-k)^2=r^2$; C(h,k); r=radius The original circle, $x^2+y^2=49$, has its center located at (0, 0) since the h and k values in the equation are both zero. Shifting left 12 will make h = -12. Shifting down 9 will make k = -9. Plug those values into the formula for the equation of a circle above. The radius did not change.
5	C	$m=\dfrac{y_2-y_1}{x_2-x_1}$ $d=\sqrt{(x_2-x_1)^2+(y_2-y_1)^2}$ Equation of a Circle: $(x-h)^2+(y-k)^2=r^2$ Midpoint $(\dfrac{x_1+x_2}{2}, \dfrac{y_1+y_2}{2})$ Using the formula for slope, we can find that the slopes are $m_{RS}=m_{TU}=\dfrac{1}{4}$; $m_{TR}=m_{US}=4$ which shows that opposite sides are parallel since opposite sides have equal slopes. Using the formula for distance, we can find that the length of the sides are RS = $\sqrt{17}$; TU=$\sqrt{17}$; RT=$\sqrt{17}$; SU=$\sqrt{17}$ which shows that all sides are congruent. A quadrilateral in which all sides are congruent and opposite sides are parallel is a rhombus.

Question No.	Answer	Detailed Explanation
6	B	$m = \dfrac{y_2 - y_1}{x_2 - x_1}$ $d = \sqrt{(x_2 - x_1)^2 + (y_2 - y_1)^2}$ Equation of a Circle: $(x-h)^2 + (y-k)^2 = r^2$ The coordinates of the center of a circle represent the h and k values (h, k) in the formula for the equation of a circle. The distance from the center to any point on the circle is the radius. We must find the distance between (-1, 4) and (2, 7). This distance, $3\sqrt{2}$, is the radius. Don't forget that the radius must be squared when it is placed into the equation of a circle.
7	A	The equation of a circle is in the form $(x-h)^2 + (y-k)^2 = r^2$. The general form of the point that is the center of a circle is (h, k), so $h = -3$, and $k = 8$. This gives us the equation $(x+3)^2 + (y-8)^2 = r^2$. The question says the circle contains the point (4,3). This means that the radius of the circle is the distance between the points (−3, 8) and (4, 3). Use the distance formula to find the radius squared. $r = \sqrt{(-3-4)^2 + (8-3)^2} = \sqrt{74}$; so $r^2 = 74$. The equation of the circle is $(x+3)^2 + (y-8)^2 = 74$. Now, substitute the points into the equation for x and y. If the result is a true statement, then the point is on the circle. Beginning with (2,15): $(-3-2)^2 + (8-15)^2 = 74$; $25 + 49 = 74$; the point is on the circle. Continuing with (−10,11): $(-3+10)^2 + (8-11)^2 = 74$; $49 + 9 \neq 74$; the point is not on the circle. Continuing with (−10,12): $(-3+10)^2 + (8-12)^2 = 74$; $49 + 16 \neq 74$; the point is not on the circle. Lastly, with (−9,15): $(-3+9)^2 + (8-15)^2 = 74$; $36 + 49 \neq 74$; the point is not on the circle.
8	D	The equation of a circle is in the form $(x-h)^2 + (y-k)^2 = r^2$. The general form of the point that is the center of a circle is (h, k), so $h = -4$, and $k = -5$. This gives us the equation $(x+4)^2 + (y+5)^2 = r^2$. The question says the circle contains the point (4, 10). This means that the radius of the circle is the distance between the points (−4,−5) and (−9,12). Use the distance formula to find the radius squared. $r = \sqrt{(-4-4)^2 + (-5-10)^2} = 17$; so $r^2 = 289$. The equation of the circle is $(x+4)^2 + (y+5)^2 = 289$. Now, substitute the points into the equation for x and y. If the result is a true statement, then the point is on the circle. Beginning with (5,9): $(-4-5)^2 + (-5-9)^2 = 289$; $81 + 196 \neq 289$; the point is not on the circle. Continuing with (−9,−15): $(-4+9)^2 + (-5+15)^2 = 289$; $25 + 100 \neq 289$; the point is not on the circle. Continuing with (−11,−19): $(-4+11)^2 + (-5+19)^2 = 289$; $49 + 196 \neq 289$; the point is not on the circle. Lastly, with (−12,−20): $(-4+12)^2 + (-5+20)^2 = 289$; $64 + 225 = 289$; the point is on the circle.

Question No.	Answer	Detailed Explanation
9	D	Rules: $m=\dfrac{y_2-y_1}{x_2-x_1}$ Formula for slope of a line $y = mx + b$ Parallel lines have slopes that are equal (but their y-intercepts are different) Perpendicular lines have slopes that are negative reciprocals. Using the formula for slope above, we find that the slope of line $i=\dfrac{4}{3}$. The slope of line $k=\dfrac{5}{8}$. The lines cannot be parallel since their slopes are not equal. The lines cannot be perpendicular since their slopes are not negative reciprocals. Therefore, the lines are neither parallel nor perpendicular.
10	A	Rules: $m=\dfrac{y_2-y_1}{x_2-x_1}$ Formula for slope of a line $y = mx + b$ Slope-intercept form of a line, where m = slope and b = y-intercept $y-y_1=m(x-x_1)$ Point-slope form of a line, where m = slope and (x_1, y_1) is a point on the line. Ax + By = C Standard Form of a Line. In order to be standard form, the x and y terms must be on the same side of the equation and there can be no fractions in the equation. Use the formula above for finding slope. The slope of the line is $\dfrac{10}{3}$. Now use the point-slope formula above to find the equation of the line. You may plug in either point as the (x_1,y_1) values in the formula. You will get the same answer either way. After simplifying the equation, move the x-term to the left so that both variables are on the same side. Now multiply every term by 3 to get rid of the fraction. Be careful to multiply EVERY term by 3.

Question No.	Answer	Detailed Explanation
11	D	If two lines are parallel, they have the same slope. The slope-intercept form of a linear equation is y=mx+b, where m is the slope and b is the $y-intercept$. The slope of the given equation y=6x-1 is 6. Since the questions asks for a line that is parallel to the given line, the answer is a line with the same slope. The question gives a point the new line must pass through, and the given equation gives the slope, so use the point-slope form of the equation to find an equation of the line. The point-slope equation of a line is $y-y_1=m(x-x_1)$, where x and y are the variables in the equation and (x_1, y_1) is the point the line passes through. Thus, the point-slope equation is y+4=6(x−2).
12	C	If two lines are perpendicular, their slopes are negative reciprocals of each other. The slope-intercept form of a linear equation is y=mx+b, where m is the slope and b is the $y-intercept$. The slope of the given equation y=x-9 is 1. Since the questions asks for a line that is perpendicular to the given line, the answer is a line with the slope of -1. The question gives a point the new line must pass through, and the given equation gives the slope, so use the point-slope form of the equation to find an equation of the line. The point-slope equation of a line is $y-y_1=m(x-x_1)$, where x and y are the variables in the equation and (x_1, y_1) is the point the line passes through. Thus, the point-slope equation is y+8=−1(x−4) or y+8=−(x−4).
13	A	Since M is the midpoint of $\overline{CD}$, that means that CM = DM. Set the two equal to each other and solve for x. The value for x is 4. Substitute 4 back into each expression to find that CM = 15 and DM = 15. Therefore, CD = 30.
14	D	$(\frac{x_1+x_2}{2}, \frac{y_1+y_2}{2})$ Midpoint Formula First we need to find the midpoint of $\overline{JK}$ using the midpoint formula above. Substitute the values for points J and K into the formula to find the R is (1, 0). This is also given to be the midpoint of $\overline{AB}$. Since we now know the coordinates of the midpoint, (1, 0), we need to find the values for (x_2, y_2). Use the midpoint formula above. Use point A for the values of x_1 and y_1. Set each part equal to the value of the midpoint and solve for x_2 and y_2.

Question No.	Answer	Detailed Explanation
15	C	Point C is at -30 on the number line in the figure, and point D is at 30. Thus, the length of segment CD is 60. To divide the segment into two parts with a ratio of their lengths of 1:2, change the ratio to 1x:2x to allow variation in the location on the number line. Next, set the sum of the two parts equal to 60 and solve for x. 1x+2x=60; 3x=60; x=20. Now, that you know that x=20, Find the value on the number line by adding 20 to the position of point C; −30+20=−10. The value on the number line that divides segment CD in a ratio of 1:2 is -10.
16	D	Point O is at -10 on the number line in the figure, and point P is at 8. Thus, the length of segment OP is 18. To divide the segment into two parts with a ratio of their lengths of 7:2, change the ratio to 7x:2x to allow variation in the location on the number line. Next, set the sum of the two parts equal to 18 and solve for x. 7x+2x=18; 9x=18; x=2. Now, that you know that x=2, find 7x, which equals 14. Find the value on the number line by adding 14 to the position of point O; −10+14=4. The value on the number line that divides segment OP in a ratio of 7:2 is 4.
17	D	A rhombus is a parallelogram with 4 congruent sides. Use the distance formula to find the length of one of the sides such as PQ = 5. Now find which of the points will have a distance of 5 between the R and S or R and Q. When R = (2,5), QR = 5 and RS = 5 which makes all 4 sides congruent.
18	C	Since a rhombus has four congruent sides, find the length of any side using the distance formula. AB = $\sqrt{9+16}$=5. Multiply the length by 4. Perimeter = 20.
19	C	The coordinates of the vertices are: point A:(2,5); point B:(2,1); and point C:(5,1). Use the distance formula, $d=\sqrt{(x_2-x_1)^2+(y_2-y_1)^2}$ to find the length of each side. The length of side AB=$\sqrt{(2-2)^2+(1-5)^2}$=4, the length of side BC=$\sqrt{(5-2)^2+(1-1)^2}$=3, and the length of side AC=$\sqrt{(5-2)^2+(1-5)^2}$=5. The sum of the sides is 4+3+5=12. The perimeter is 12.

Question No.	Answer	Detailed Explanation
20	A	The coordinates of the vertices are: point X:$(-4,-1)$; point Y:$(2,-1)$; and point Z:$(-1,4)$. Use the distance formula, $d=\sqrt{(x_2-x_1)^2+(y_2-y_1)^2}$ to find the length of each side. The length of side XY$=\sqrt{(2-(-4))^2+(-1-(1))^2}=6$, the length of side YZ$=\sqrt{(-1-2)^2+(4-(-1))^2}=\sqrt{34}$, and the length of side XZ$=\sqrt{(-1-(-4))^2+(4-(-1))^2}=\sqrt{34}$. The sum of the sides is $6+\sqrt{34}+\sqrt{34}=6+2\sqrt{34}$. The perimeter is $6+2\sqrt{34}$.

Chapter 5 - Geometric Measurement & Dimension

Question No.	Answer	Detailed Explanation
1	D	The space left in the can in the difference between the volume of the can and the volume of the sphere according to: $\Delta V = \pi r^2 h - (4/3)\pi r^3$ $\Delta V = \pi(6cm)^2(10cm) - (4/3)\pi(6cm)^3$ $\Delta V = 72\pi cm^3$
2	C	The fraction of the volume occupied by the cone is the ratio of the volume of the cone to the volume of the can. $\dfrac{1/3\pi r2h}{\pi r2h} = \dfrac{1}{3}$
3	D	The volume of the hopper is the difference between the full volume of the full pyramid and the volume of the truncated region. The width of the base of the truncated region is found by proportion as $(3m/15m) \times (5m) = 1m$. $V = (1/3Bh)_{pyramid} - (1/3Bh)_{truncated}$ $V = (1/3)(5m \times 5m)(15m) - (1/3)(1m \times 1m)(3m)$ $V = 124m^3$
4	A	The fraction of the volume occupied by the volume is equal to the ratio of the volume of the liquid to the volume of the cone. The cone formed by the liquid has radius r and height h by proportion. Fraction $= \dfrac{1/3\pi r^2 h}{1/3\pi R^2 H}$ where R = radius of cone = 2r and H = height of cone = 2h. Fraction $= \dfrac{1/3\pi r^2 h}{1/3\pi(2r)^2(2h)}$ Fraction = 1/8
5	C	The volume held by the cone is $1/3\pi r^2 h$. The volume of the cone will be equal to the cylinder of fluid formed when poured into the can. The cylinder of fluid has volume $\pi r^2 h'$ where h' is the depth of the fluid. Therefore: $1/3\pi r^2 h = \pi r^2 h' h' = 1/3h \, rh'/h = 1/3$
6	C	The volume of a cylinder is given by: $V = 1/3\pi r^2 h$ The volume of a cone is given by: $V = 1/3\pi r^2 h$ The volume of a pyramid is given by: $V = 1/3 \, B \, h$ The volume of a sphere is given by: $V = 4/3\pi r^3$

Question No.	Answer	Detailed Explanation
7	C	Use the formula for volume of a cylinder: $V=\pi r^2 h$. In this case the radius (r) can be found by dividing the diameter in half. If the diameter is 2 meters then the radius will be 1 meter ($\frac{2m}{2}=1m$). The height (h) is given as 3 meters. This information can now be substituted into the formula. $V=\pi r^2 h$ $V=\pi(1m)^2 3m=3.14(1m^2)(3m)=9.42m^3$
8	A	The formula for the volume of a cone is $V=\pi r^2\frac{h}{3}$. The height (h) is given as 2 feet. The radius (r) can be found by dividing the diameter in half. The radius is then $\frac{4m}{2}=2m$. These values can then be substituted into the formula. $V=\pi r^2\frac{h}{3}$ $V=(3.14)(2m)^2\frac{2m}{3}=(3.14)(4m^2)(\frac{2}{3}m)=8.373m^3$
9	B	Since the assumption is made in the problem that the snowball is a perfect sphere the formula for the volume of a sphere can be used $V=\pi r^3$. The radius (r) will be ½ the diameter or ($\frac{5in}{2}=2.5in$). Substituting this value into the formula… $V=\frac{4}{3}\pi r^3=\frac{4}{3}(3.14)(2.5in)^3=\frac{4}{3}(3.14)(15.625in^3)=65.42in^3$ Of the possible choices 65 in^3 is closest to 65.42 in^3.
10	A	Sphere with radius 5 mm = $V=\pi r^3=\pi(5\text{ mm})^3=125\pi\text{ mm}^3$ Cone with height of 6 cm and radius of 7 cm = $V=\pi r^2\frac{h}{3}=\pi(7cm)^2\frac{6cm}{2}=98\pi cm^3$ Rectangular Pyramid with height of 1 ft, length of 10 ft, and base of 5 ft. = $V=\frac{lbh}{3}=\frac{(1ft)(5ft)(10ft)}{3}=16.67ft^3$ Cylinder with radius of 8 cm and height of 9 cm = $V=\pi r^2 h=\pi(8\text{ cm})^2(9cm)=576\pi$
11	C	The cross section would have the same shape as the faces of the cube, so it would be a square.
12	B	The cross section would have the same shape as the base, therefore it is a circle.
13	D	The figure formed is a rectangle of dimensions 7 cm x 12 cm. The area is A = L * W ; therefore A = (7 cm)(12 cm) = $84cm^2$.

Question No.	Answer	Detailed Explanation
14	C	Since the perimeter is the sum of the three equal sides, each side has length 10 cm. The altitude bisects the side of the triangle opposite the vertex it is drawn from. By use of the Pythagorean theorem, the altitude will have length $x = \sqrt{(10cm)^2 - (5cm)^2} = \sqrt{75}$cm). The object generated will be a cone with radius 5 cm and height $\sqrt{75}$cm. The volume of the object is $V = 1/3\pi r^2 h$. Therefore the volume is $V = (1/3)\pi(5cm)^2\sqrt{75}cm = \frac{125\sqrt{3}}{3}\pi cm^3$.
15	C	The circle will have a radius of 3 cm since the area $A=\pi r^2$. The object generated will be a sphere whose volume is calculated from $V=4/3\pi r^3$. Therefore the volume of the generated sphere will be $V=(4/3)\pi(3cm)^3=36\pi cm^3$.
16	B	Slicing the cylinder through the middle would result in a circle. 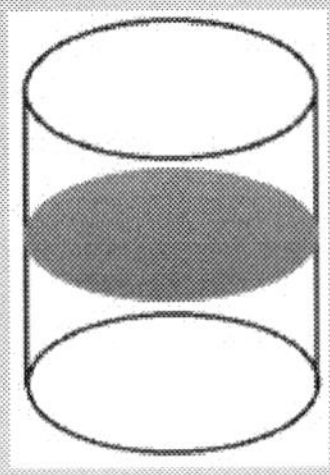
17	B	Cutting the triangular prism in the fashion shown below would result in an equilateral triangle. 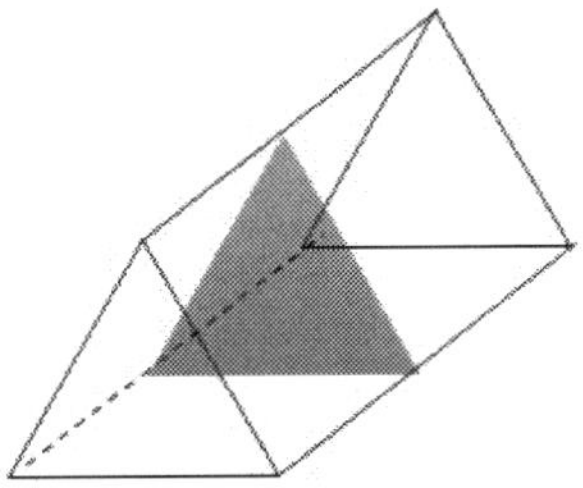
18	A	The only shape that can result from the cross section of a sphere is a circle. 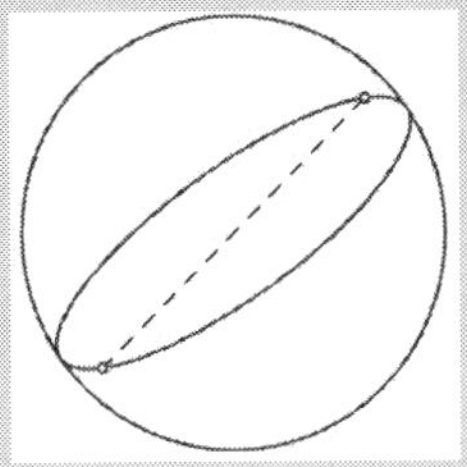

Question No.	Answer	Detailed Explanation
19	C	
20	A	Looking from above the figure the viewer would see the top row on cubes.

Chapter 6 - Modeling with Geometry

Rules for Question No. 1 to 5:

Rules: $c^2 = a^2 + b^2$ Pythagorean Theorem
$A = s^2$ Area of a Square
$A = \frac{bh}{2}$ Area of a Triangle
$A = lw$ Area of a Rectangle
$A = \pi r^2$ Area of a Circle
$C = 2\pi r$ or $C = \pi d$ Circumference of a Circle
$V = \frac{4}{3}\pi r^3$ Volume of a Sphere
$V = Bh = lwh$ Volume of a Rectangular Prism
$V = Bh = \pi r^2 h$ Volume of a Cylinder
$S = 2\pi r^2 + 2\pi rh$ Surface Area of a Cylinder

Question No.	Answer	Detailed Explanation
1	D	The perimeter of a figure is found by adding all of the sides together. Since a square has 4 congruent sides, we can multiply the length of the side, 15 ft, times 4 to get 60 ft.
2	B	Use the formula for the area of a triangle above. The legs of a right triangle are the base and the height. 154.875 rounds to 155 when rounding to the nearest whole number.
3	C	To find the perimeter of a figure, we must add the length of each side. To find the missing side of the triangle, we need to use the Pythagorean Theorem and find the hypotenuse, c. The hypotenuse is $5\sqrt{5} \approx 11.2$. Then add all three sides together to get the perimeter.
4	C	To find the area of a circle using the formula above, we need to know the radius of the circle. Since the radius is ½ the diameter, the radius is 2.5 cm. Plug 2.5 cm into the formula for area of a circle above. $A \approx 20$ cm².
5	A	A globe is in the shape of a sphere. To find the volume of a sphere, we need the radius of the sphere. Since the radius is ½ of the diameter, the radius is 40 mm. Use the formula for volume of a sphere above. Plug in the radius. $V = 268,082$ mm³.

Question No.	Answer	Detailed Explanation
6	B	Remember the formula for perimeter is the sum of the length of the sides. For a square where all sides are equal: $P=4s$ Substituting the value for perimeter $4\,ft=4s$ $1\,ft=s$ If each side measures 1 ft. The area will be: $A=s^2$ Substituting the value of s: $A=(1ft)^2=1ft^2$
7	D	Since the spheres touch the side of the cylinder the radius of the sphere is equal to the radius of the cylinder. The height of the cylinder will be the sum of the radii of the 4 spheres times two or $2(4r)=8r$. $V=\pi r^2 h$ $V=\pi(4cm)^2(8\times4cm)=\pi\times16cm^2\times32cm=512\pi cm^3$
8	B	$V = Bh = lwh$ Volume of a Rectangular Prism The formula for density is $d = m/V$. The volume is given to be $310\ cm^3$ and the mass is 853 g. Plug those values into the formula to find density.
9	A	$d=\dfrac{m}{V}$ Density Plug the given values into the density formula above. Rearrange and solve for m, $m = dV$; $m=3.26g/cm^3(.275cm^3) = 0.897g$.
10	A	$d=\dfrac{m}{V}$ Density Plug the given values into the density formula above. Rearrange and solve for V, $V = m/d = 85.4\ g/ 13.6g/mL = 6.28mL$.
11	A	The formula for density is $d=\dfrac{m}{V}$. Plug the values into the formula. Divide the values to find the density. $\dfrac{96.2g}{32.3\ cm^3} = 2.98g/cm^3$
12	C	$d=\dfrac{m}{V}$ Density Use the formula for density above. Plug the given values into the formula in the appropriate places. Solve for V. $\dfrac{48.4g}{6.3\ cm^3} = 7.68\ cm^3$.

Question No.	Answer	Detailed Explanation
13	C	Use conversions to find the weight of the water. $\dfrac{8.3 \text{ lb}}{\text{gallon}} \times 10 \text{ gallons} = 83 \text{ lbs}$
14	B	Density is found using the formula $p = \dfrac{m}{V}$ While the mass is known, 52 grams, the volume is unknown. However, it can be calculated using the formula for volume of a sphere. $V = \dfrac{4}{3}\pi r^3 = \dfrac{4}{3}(3.14)(8\text{cm})^3 = 2143.57\text{cm}^3$ Now density can be found $p = \dfrac{m}{V} = \dfrac{52 \text{ g}}{2143.57\text{cm}^3} = .02\dfrac{\text{g}}{\text{cm}^3}$
15	B	Let x = length of short side, x + 4 = length of medium side, 2x + 2 = length of longest side. x + (x + 4) + (2x + 2) = 38 cm. Solving the equation for x yields x = 8 cm which is the length of the short side.
16	C	The initial volume of the prism is x^2h. If the dimensions of the prism are doubled, the new volume would be $(2x)^2(2h)=8x^2h$. The increase in volume is $8x^2h-x^2h=315\text{cm}^3$; $7x^2h=315\text{cm}^3$; $x^2h=45\text{cm}^3$ which is the initial volume of the prism.
17	B	The initial surface area of the cube is $6x^2$. If the lengths of the sides were doubled, the new surface area would be $6(2x)^2=24x^2$. The change in surface area is $24x^2-6x^2=18x^2$; $18x^2=162\text{cm}^2$. Solving for x yields x = 3 cm.
18	C	The initial dimensions of the rectangle are w x 2w which gives an area of $2w^2$. If the length and width are each increased by 2 cm, the dimensions become (w + 2) x (2w + 2) which has an area of $2w^2+6w+4$. The increase in area is $(2w^2+6w+4)-(2w^2)=52\text{cm}^2$. Solving for w yields w = 8 cm.
19	D	The box will have dimension (20cm - 2(4cm)) x (16 cm - 2(4 cm)) x 4 cm. V = lwh ; V = (12 cm)(8 cm)(4 cm) = 384cm^3
20	B	The shaded area is the difference between the area of the square and the area of the quarter circle. A = (4cm)(4cm) − ¼(π)(4 cm)^2 = 3.43 cm^2.

Chapter 7 - Conditional Probability and the Rules of Probability

Question No.	Answer	Detailed Explanation
1	C	The probability of an event is the number of successful responses divided by the number of total responses. The table gives the responses on the participants' preferences. A successful response is that the new car buyer prefers a Candy Apple Red car with a V8. There is 500 total response. Therefore, the probability is $\frac{105}{500} = \frac{21}{100} = 21\%$
2	B	The union of two sets is the set of all members that are in either set. The question states that Set A = {1, 2, 3, 4, 5}. Set B = {1, 2, 3}. Put the two sets together for the union and A ∪ B = {1, 2, 3, 4, 5}. The intersection of two sets is the set of all members that are in both sets. . The question states that Set A = {1, 2, 3, 4, 5}. Set B = {1, 2, 3}. The set of all members that are in both sets is A ∩ B = {1, 2, 3}
3	B	The set of {:H. Even number} is the set containing elements of the sample space that do not contain H and have an even number. The sample space is the set {T1,H1,T2,H2,T3,H3T4, H4,T5,H5,T6,H6}. The elements that do not have H is the set {T1,T2,T3,T4,T5,T6} and the elements of that set that do not have H and have an even number is the set {T2,T4,T6}.
4	B	Since a standard deck of playing cards has 52 cards, with 13 hearts, 13 clubs, 13 spades, and 13 diamonds, the probability of picking the first diamond is $\frac{13}{52}$ or $\frac{1}{4}$. Since you did not replace the first card back into the deck, the number of diamonds in the deck changed from 13 to 12 and the number of cards in the deck changed from 52 to 51. The probability of selecting a second diamond is $\frac{12}{51}$. Since this probability is different from the first probability, the two events, picking the first diamond and picking the second diamond are dependent events.
5	D	Since a standard deck of playing cards has 52 cards, with 13 hearts, 13 clubs, 13 spades, and 13 diamonds, the probability of picking the first spade is $\frac{13}{52}$ or $\frac{1}{4}$. Since you replace the first card back into the deck, the number of spades in the deck does not change and the number of cards in the deck does not change. The probability of selecting a second spade is $\frac{13}{52}$ or $\frac{1}{4}$. Since this probability is the same as the first probability, the two events, picking the first spade and picking the second spade are independent events.

Question No.	Answer	Detailed Explanation
6	B	Two events are independent of each other if the probability of the first event times the probability of the second event is equal to the probabilities of both events occurring together, which is the product of their probabilities. The probability of reaching into the bag and drawing out a purple marble is $\frac{25}{50}=\frac{1}{2}$ because the bag contains 25 purple marbles out of 50 marbles. The probability of reaching into the bag and drawing out another purple marble is $\frac{24}{49}$ because the bag contains 24 purple marbles out of 49 marbles. The probability of drawing two purple marbles could be written as a single compound probability. Thus, the probability of both of these events occurring is P(purple, purple) = P(purple). P(purple) $\frac{1}{2} \cdot \frac{1}{2} = \frac{1}{4}$ This probability is not the same as the product of the original probabilities, so the two events are dependent of each other. This is because not replacing the purple marble changes the original probability of drawing another purple marble because the number of marbles in the back is reduced by one. If the first purple marble is replaced, then the two events are independent.
7	C	The question states that Juan has 25 coins in a bag, including 10 dimes and 15 quarters. He reaches into the bag and pulls out a coin. Then he reaches into the bag again and pulls out another coin. We are asked to find the probability that Juan pulls out a quarter as the second coin, given that he pulls out a quarter as the first coin as well. This is called conditional probability, which is calculated by calculating the number of coins in the bag after the first quarter is pulled from the bag. If Juan pulls a quarter out of the bag, then the bag has 24 coins, including 10 dimes and 14 quarters. The probability of pulling a second quarter out of the bag is $\frac{14}{24}=\frac{7}{12}$
8	D	The table shows the result of the survey. The question asks us to find the probability that a randomly selected student is interested in hiking given the condition that the student is a girl. This is called conditional probability, which is calculated by P(Hiking|Girl)=$\frac{P(Hiking \cap Girl)}{P(Girl)}$. From the table, P(Hiking$\cap$Girl)=$\frac{50}{250}$ and P(Girl)=$\frac{113}{250}$. Therefore, P(Hiking|Girl)=$\frac{\frac{50}{250}}{\frac{113}{250}}=\frac{50}{113}$.

Question No.	Answer	Detailed Explanation
9	D	The question states that Juan has 30 coins in a bag, including 12 dimes and 18 quarters. He reaches into the bag and pulls out a coin. Then he reaches into the bag again and pulls out another coin. We are asked to find the probability that Juan pulls out a quarter as the second coin, given that he pulls out a quarter as the first coin as well. This is called conditional probability, which is calculated by calculating the number of coins in the bag after the first quarter is pulled from the bag. If Juan pulls a quarter out of the bag, then the bag has 29 coins, including 12 dimes and 17 quarters. The probability of pulling a second quarter out of the bag is $\frac{17}{29}$.
10	B	In the two-way table, rows and columns must add across and down. In the first row, we will find X by subtracting $94 - 73 = 21$. In the second row, we will find Y by subtracting $94 - 59 = 35$. The third row contains the column totals, so we can find Z by adding $94 + 94 = 188$ or by adding $80 + 108 = 188$.
11	C	The two-way table shows that 151 men were surveyed and 92 of them preferred to work at home. Find the number of men who preferred to work in the office by subtracting $151 - 92 = 59$. The survey also shows that 99 women were surveyed and 81 of them preferred to work at the office. Find the number of women who preferred to work at home by subtracting $99 - 81 = 18$.
12	A	In the two-way table, rows and columns must add across and down. D and E are column totals, so if we find the totals of the two columns, we have their values. The two-way table shows that 6 fifth graders and 4 sixth grades do their homework with a pen. We can find D by adding $6 + 4 = 10$. The table also shows that 29 fifth graders and 21 sixth grades do their homework with a pencil. Therefore, find E by adding $29 + 21 = 50$. The letter F is the total of the two columns put together. Thus, we will find F by adding $10 + 50 = 60$.
13	B	The length of $\overline{AE}$ is $21-9=12$ units long. The length of $\overline{BC}$ is $15-12=3$ units long. The probability that the point on $\overline{AE}$ is on $\overline{BC}$ is $\frac{m\overline{BC}}{m\overline{AE}}=\frac{3}{12}=\frac{1}{4}$.
14	A	Answer choice A is the only one that doesn't work for this problem situation. There is no mention of brown hair and there are many other colors of hair that are not blonde so this is not a good label for this problem situation.
15	D	The probability of two events both occurring is the sum of the probability of either occurring.

Question No.	Answer	Detailed Explanation
16	A	The report shows that in a high school with 400 students, there are 40% girls. The report says that 20% of the students in the school wear glasses. It is also known that 10% of the boys wear glasses. We are asked to determine how many boys wear glasses. If 40% of the students at the school are girls, then 60% are boys. This means there are 400-60% = 240 boys in the school. Then, since 10% of the boys wear glasses, 240-10% = 24 boys wear glasses.
17	B	The report shows that in a high school with 400 students, there are 40% girls. The report says that 20% of the students in the school wear glasses. It is also known that 10% of the boys wear glasses. We are asked to determine how many boys are at the school. If 40% of the students at the school are girls, then 60% of the students are boys. This means there are 400-60% = 240 boys in the school.
18	A	The question says a study found that in a small town, 40% of all households have a pet and 35% have children living at home. The report also found that 60% of all households with children living at home have a pet. We are asked to find if the probability that a household has children living at home and has a pet if that household in the town is selected at random. This means we want the probability of a family having children living at home AND having a pet. An AND system in probabilities, means we multiply the probabilities. We know that 35% of all households have children living at home and 60% of those families have a pet. So we are looking for 35% - 60% = 21%. The answer is 21% of all families in the small town have children living at home and have a pet.
19	C	The probability that event C occurs or that event D occurs is calculated by adding the probability that event C occurs to the probability that event D occurs and then subtracting the probability that events C and D both occur. This probability is calculated by $P(C \text{ or } D)=P(C)+P(D)-P(C \text{ and } D)$. We know that $P(C)=0.4, P(D)=0.6$, and $P(C \text{ and } D)=0.2$. Therefore, $P(C)+P(D)-P(C \text{ and } D)=0.4+0.6-0.2=0.8$.
20	D	The probability that event G occurs or that event H occurs is calculated by adding the probability that event G occurs to the probability that event H occurs and then subtracting the probability that events G and H both occur. This probability is calculated by $P(G \text{ or } H)=P(G)+P(H)-P(G \text{ and } H)$. We know that $P(G)=0.35, P(H)=0.45$, and $P(G \text{ and } H)=0.25$. Therefore, $P(G)+P(H)-P(G \text{ and } H)=0.35+0.45-0.25=0.55$.

Chapter 8 - Using Probability to Make Decisions

Question No.	Answer	Detailed Explanation
1	D	To be a fair decision, any items used in the process should not be different in any way.
2	C	Both A and B are fair ways to randomly make a decision with no bias in any direction.
3	D	The coin could certainly be fair or unfair as it is not specified in the question as being one way or the other. This result could also just be due to chance as a coin flip could land on the same thing an infinite number of times theoretically.
4	D	The explanation could certainly be any of these answer choices. The best way to rule out differences between this ball and the others is to investigate the ball in question or perhaps replace it altogether.
5	B	Answer choices A and C are certainly biased towards you mom or dad. Choice D seems like it might work but having a person choose even if they don't have any interest in the situation is flawed because they could be manipulated. This leaves choice B as the best answer.
6	A	The number of sides really has nothing to do with fairness. The fact that there is no bias as to how it lands makes it a fair way to make a decision.
7	C	Ever heard of having a good poker face? Psychology and manipulation play too much of a factor in poker games for this to be a fair decision making strategy.
8	B	The best way is to draw lots with one restaurant listed for each lot. Flipping a coin won't work as well because there are 3 choices and only 2 sides. You would have to flip more than once. Rolling a six sided die would also be confusing since there are only 3 choices but six sides. Obviously letting the driver pick would be biased.
9	A	Making small inconsequential decisions via the methods we have discussed is fine. Making a life or death decision via probability of any kind is unwise and unfair.
10	B	If the sign on the cucumber bin advertises a price of $10 per dozen, then each cucumber should cost approximately $.83 each. Understandably, the manager could round the charge to minimize change requirements, but charging $1.33 per cucumber is not fair. The only situation that might make this fair is for the sign to state that the listed price was a "special" deal.

Question No.	Answer	Detailed Explanation
11	C	In the grand scheme of things, this litigation cost is small compared to all the other costs the car manufacturer must consider. Basing the price of their cars on something so small would be silly.
12	B	No just the fact that people are swimming during a thunderstorm puts them at higher risk. Also since water conducts electricity anyone in the pool with the person who got struck would also be electrocuted so this is not a fair assumption.
13	A	The lack of random assignment could introduce bias into the study. When possible, all forms of bias should be removed from the study to ensure that it is fair.
14	D	By collecting samples from all of these groups the results would be more complete and would most likely be non-biased.
15	A	Since the expected value of the bet is less than the actual value of the bet, the player will end up with losses in the long run. Hence, answer choice A is correct.
16	B	When coming up with empirical probabilities, the best plan is to gather data through random sampling of the population. A research and focus group would accomplish this.
17	C	In most cases, small samples will not provide empirical data that is as accurate as large samples. The larger the sample size, the more randomness and variation are involved.
18	C	Tossing a coin does nothing to tell the company about the soil in either county. Asking county officials would definitely introduce bias. Taking samples of the soil and running studies on those results would be the best way for the geologist to inform himself about the soil in the two counties.
19	B	To determine which bet is a better deal, calculate the expected value of each bet and subtract the cost of the bet. Expected value is the probability of winning the payout times the amount of the payout. Whichever bet has a larger net expected value is the better deal. For Bet A, the expected value is $13/25 \times 18 = 15.60$; $15.60 - 10 = 5.60$. For Bet B, the expected value is $6/25 \times 100 = 24$; $24 - 15 = 9$. Bet B is the better deal.

Question No.	Answer	Detailed Explanation
20	A	To determine which raffle is a better deal, calculate the expected value of each raffle and subtract the cost of the ticket. Expected value is the probability of winning the payout times the amount of the payout. Whichever raffle has a larger net expected value is the better deal. For Raffle A, the expected value is $1/1000 \times 1000 = 1$; $1 - 3 = -2$. For Raffle B, There are three chances to win, so the expected value is $1/250 \times 300 + 1/249 \times 150 + 1/248 \times 75 = 2.10$; $2.10 - 5 = -2.90$ Raffle A is the better deal.

High School Math FAQs

What will Geometry Assessment Look Like?

In many ways, the Geometry assessments will be unlike anything many students have ever seen. The tests require students to complete tasks to assess a deeper understanding of the CCSS in domains such as Geometry and Statistics.

What are the Math credit programs offered in High Schools?

Most of the High Schools offer Algebra 1, Algebra 2, Geometry, Integrated Math 1 and Integrated Math 2.

What item types are included in the Online Geometry Test?

Because the assessment is online, the test will consist of a combination of new types of questions:

1. Drag and Drop
2. Drop Down
3. Essay Response
4. Extended Constructed Response
5. Hot Text Select and Drag
6. Hot Text Selective Highlight
7. Matching Table In-line
8. Matching Table Single Response
9. Multiple Choice – Single Correct Response, radial buttons
10. Multiple Choice – Multiple Response, checkboxes
11. Numeric Response
12. Short Text
13. Table Fill-in

What if I buy more than one Lumos Study Program?

Step 1

Visit the URL and login to your account.
http://www.lumoslearning.com

Step 2

Click on 'My tedBooks' under the "Account" tab.
Place the Book Access Code and submit.

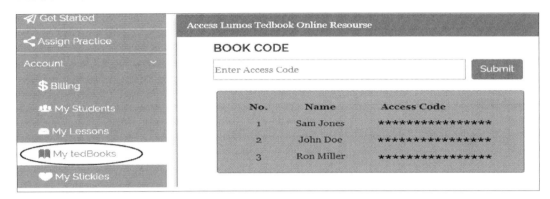

Step 3

To add the new book for a registered student, choose the
◉ Existing Student button and select the student and submit.

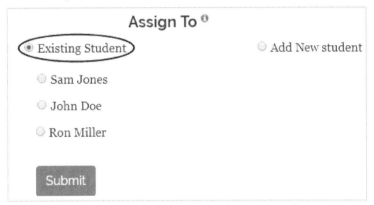

To add the new book for a new student, choose the ◯ Add New student
button and complete the student registration.

Register Your TedBook

Student Name: *	Enter First Name	Enter Last Name
Student Login *		
Password *		

Submit

Lumos StepUp® Mobile App FAQ For Students

What is the Lumos StepUp® App?

It is a FREE application you can download onto your Android Smartphones, tablets, iPhones, and iPads.

What are the Benefits of the StepUp® App?

This mobile application gives convenient access to Practice Tests, Common Core State Standards, Online Workbooks, and learning resources through your Smartphone and tablet computers.

- Eleven Technology enhanced question types in both MATH and ELA
- Sample questions for Arithmetic drills
- Standard specific sample questions
- Instant access to the Common Core State Standards
- Jokes and cartoons to make learning fun!

Do I Need the StepUp® App to Access Online Workbooks?

No, you can access Lumos StepUp® Online Workbooks through a personal computer. The StepUp® app simply enhances your learning experience and allows you to conveniently access StepUp® Online Workbooks and additional resources through your smart phone or tablet.

How can I Download the App?

Visit **lumoslearning.com/a/stepup-app** using your Smartphone or tablet and follow the instructions to download the app.

QR Code
for Smartphone
Or Tablet Users

Lumos StepUp® Mobile App FAQ
For Parents and Teachers

What is the Lumos StepUp® App?

It is a free app that teachers can use to easily access real-time student activity information as well as assign learning resources to students. Parents can also use it to easily access school-related information such as homework assigned by teachers and PTA meetings. It can be downloaded onto smart phones and tablets from popular App Stores.

What are the Benefits of the Lumos StepUp® App?

It provides convenient access to

- Standards aligned learning resources for your students
- An easy to use Dashboard
- Student progress reports
- Active and inactive students in your classroom
- Professional development information
- Educational Blogs

How can I Download the App?

Visit **lumoslearning.com/a/stepup-app** using your Smartphone or tablet and follow the instructions to download the app.

QR Code
for Smartphone
Or Tablet Users

Progress Chart

Standard	Lesson	Q No.	Page No.	Practice		Mastered	Re-practice /Reteach
				Date	Score		
	Chapter 1: Congruence		57				
G.CO.1	Introduction to geometry, Geometry definitions	1					
		2					
G.CO.2	Transformations in the coordinate plane	3					
		4					
G.CO.3	Rotational and line symmetry	5					
		6					
G.CO.4	Defining Transformations	7					
		8					
G.CO.5	Graphing Transformations on a coordinate plane	9					
		10					
G.CO.6	Transformations and congruence	11					
		12					
G.CO.7	Transformations and congruent triangles	13					
		14					
G.CO.8	Triangle congruencies	15					
		16					
G.CO.9	Lines and Angles	17					
G.CO.10	Triangles and their angles	18					
G.CO.11	Parallelograms	19					
G.CO.13	Polygons inscribed in a circle	20					
	Chapter 2: Similarity, Right Triangles, and Trigonometry		64				
G-SRT.1a G-SRT.1b	Triangles & Rectangles	1					
		2					
		3					
G-SRT.2	Similarity Transformations	4					
		5					
		6					

Standard	Lesson	Q No.	Page No.	Practice		Mastered	Re-practice /Reteach
				Date	Score		
G-SRT.3	AA similarity	7					
		8					
		9					
G-SRT.4	Theorems about Triangles	10					
		11					
		12					
G-SRT.5	Triangles Congruence Statements	13					
		14					
G-SRT.6	Triangle Similarity Statements	15					
		16					
G-SRT.7	Sine and Cosine of Complementary Angles	17					
		18					
G-SRT.8	Applications of The Pythagorean Theorem and Trigonometry	19					
		20					
	Chapter 3: Circles		**72**				
G.C.1	Similarity of Circles	1					
		2					
		3					
		4					
		5					
G.C.2	Angles, Radii, and Chords	6					
		7					
		8					
		9					
		10					
G.C.3	Construct the inscribed and circumscribed circles of a triangle	11					
		12					
		13					
		14					

Standard	Lesson	Q No.	Page No.	Practice		Mastered	Re-practice /Reteach
				Date	Score		
		15					
G.C.5	Concepts related to sectors of a circle	16					
		17					
		18					
		19					
		20					
	Chapter 4: Expressing Geometric Properties with Equations		**79**				
G-GPE.1	Equation of a circle	1					
		2					
		3					
		4					
G-GPE.4	Use coordinates to prove simple geometric theorems	5					
		6					
		7					
		8					
G-GPE.5	Prove the slope criteria	9					
		10					
		11					
		12					
G-GPE.6	Find the point on a directed line segment	13					
		14					
		15					
		16					
G-GPE.7	Use coordinates to compute perimeters of polygons	17					
		18					
		19					
		20					

Standard	Lesson	Q No.	Page No.	Practice		Mastered	Re-practice /Reteach
				Date	Score		
	Chapter 5: Geometric Measurement & Dimension		84				
G-GMD.3	Finding volume of cylinders, pyramids, cones and spheres	1					
		2					
		3					
		4					
		5					
		6					
		7					
		8					
		9					
		10					
G-GMD.4	Understanding the relationships between 2D and 3D	11					
		12					
		13					
		14					
		15					
		16					
		17					
		18					
		19					
		20					
	Chapter 6: Modeling with Geometry		89				
G-MG.1	Describing objects and their properties	1					
		2					
		3					
		4					
		5					
		6					
		7					

Standard	Lesson	Q No.	Page No.	Practice		Mastered	Re-practice /Reteach
				Date	Score		
G-MG.2	Density based on area and volume	8					
		9					
		10					
		11					
		12					
		13					
		14					
G-MG.3	Geometric Design Problems	15					
		16					
		17					
		18					
		19					
		20					
	Chapter 7: Conditional Probability and the Rules of Probability		94				
S.CP.1	Describe events as subsets of a sample space	1					
		2					
		3					
S.CP.2	Probability of Independent and Dependent Events	4					
		5					
		6					
S.CP.3	Understanding conditional probability	7					
		8					
		9					
S.CP.4	Construct and Interpret Two-way Frequency Tables	10					
		11					
		12					
S.CP.5	Recognize and Explain Conditional Probability	13					

Standard	Lesson	Q No.	Page No.	Practice		Mastered	Re-practice /Reteach
				Date	Score		
		14					
		15					
S.CP.6	Finding Conditional Probability	16					
		17					
		18					
S.CP.7	Applying the Addition Rule and Interpreting Answers	19					
		20					
	Chapter 8: Using Probability to Make Decisions		**100**				
S-MD.6	Using Probabilities to Make Fair Decisions	1					
		2					
		3					
		4					
		5					
		6					
		7					
		8					
		9					
		10					
S-MD.7	Analyzing Decisions and Strategies	11					
		12					
		13					
		14					
		15					
		16					
		17					
		18					
		19					
		20					

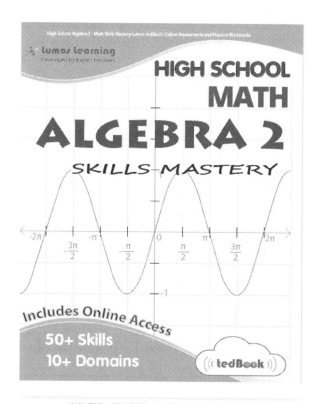

Available
- At Leading book stores
- Online www.LumosLearning.com